INTRODUCING
MATH!
GRADE 6
BY ARGOPREP

FREE VIDEO EXPLANATIONS

600 QUESTIONS TO PRACTICE

TEACHER RECOMMENDED

TOPICS COVERED
PRACTICE MAKES PERFECT

- Ratios & Proportional Relationships
- The Number System
- Expressions & Equations
- Geometry
- Statistics & Probability

ArgoPrep is one of the leading providers of supplemental educational products and services. We offer affordable and effective test prep solutions to educators, parents and students. Learning should be fun and easy! For that reason, most of our workbooks come with detailed video answer explanations taught by one of our fabulous instructors.

Our goal is to make your life easier, so let us know how we can help you by e-mailing us at: info@argoprep.com.

ISBN: 978-1946755896
Published by Argo Brothers, Inc.

Acknowledgments: Icons made by Freepik, Creaticca Creative Agency, Pixel perfect , Pixel Buddha, Smashicons, Twitter , Good Ware, Smalllikeart, Nikita Golubev, monkik, DinosoftLabs, Icon Pond from www.flaticon.com

ArgoPrep has won over 10+ educational awards for their workbooks and online learning platform. Here are a few highlighted awards!

ARGOPREP

OTHER BOOKS BY ARGOPREP

Here are some other test prep workbooks by ArgoPrep you may be interested in. All of our workbooks come equipped with detailed video explanations to make your learning experience a breeze! Visit us at *www.argoprep.com*

COMMON CORE MATH SERIES

COMMON CORE ELA SERIES

INTRODUCING MATH!

Introducing Math! by ArgoPrep is an award-winning series created by certified teachers to provide students with high-quality practice problems. Our workbooks include topic overviews with instruction, practice questions, answer explanations along with digital access to video explanations. Practice in confidence - with ArgoPrep!

SCIENCE SERIES

Science Daily Practice Workbook by ArgoPrep is an award-winning series created by certified science teachers to help build mastery of foundational science skills. Our workbooks explore science topics in depth with ArgoPrep's 5 E'S to build science mastery.

TABLE OF CONTENTS

HOW TO USE THE BOOK

Welcome to the **Introducing Math!** series by ArgoPrep.
This workbook is designed to provide you with a comprehensive overview of Grade 6 mathematics.

While working through this workbook, be sure to read the topic overview that will give you a general foundation of the concept. At the end of each chapter, there is a chapter test that will assess how well you understood the topics presented.

This workbook comes with free digital video explanations that you can access on our website. If you are unsure on how to answer a question, we strongly recommend watching the video explanations as it will reinforce the fundamental concepts.

We strive to provide you with an amazing learning experience. If you have any suggestions or need further assistance, don't hesitate to email us at info@argoprep.com or chat with us live on our website at www.argoprep.com

HOW TO WATCH VIDEO EXPLANATIONS
IT IS ABSOLUTELY FREE

Go to argoprep.com/intro6
OR scan QR Code below:

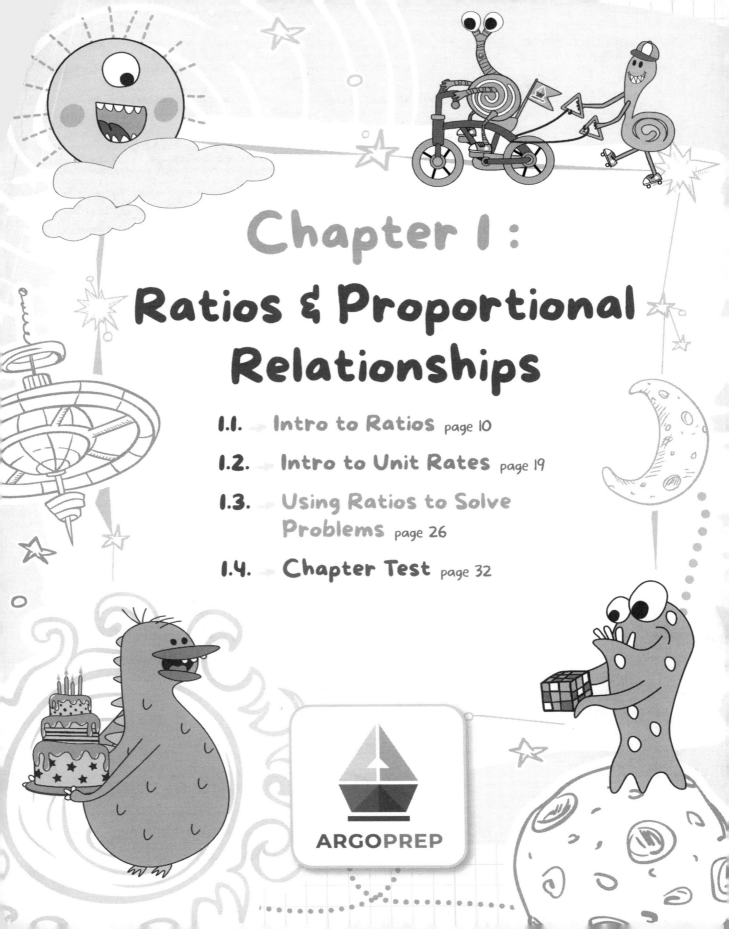

Chapter 1:
Ratios & Proportional Relationships

ARGOPREP

Understanding Ratios

A **ratio** expresses the relationship between two quantities.

Look at the shapes below. We can see that there are some hearts as well as some stars, but what is the ratio of stars to hearts?

<u>Step 1</u>: Calculate the first quantity

First we need to calculate the number of stars because the question is asking the ratio of "stars" to "hearts".

There are **2 stars**

<u>Step 2</u>: Calculate the second quantity

Next, we need to calculate the number of hearts.

There are **3 hearts**

<u>Step 3</u>: Express the relationship between the first and second quantities

The relationship can be expressed as:

The ratio of stars to hearts is **2:3**

We can also say:

For every **2** stars there are **3** hearts
or
2 to **3**

Let's look at a more challenging example.

What is the ratio of stars to hearts?

<u>Step 1</u>: First we calculate the number of stars, which is **3**.

<u>Step 2</u>: Next we calculate the number of hearts, which is **6**.

<u>Step 3</u>: Now, we express the relationship as **3:6**.

<u>Step 4</u>: We can simplify the ratio just as we simplify fractions.

The common factor is **3**. So, the ratio of stars to hearts is **1:2**.

<u>Step 5</u>: You can check your answer by looking at the quantities

We can see that for every **1** star, there are **2** hearts ✓

11

Practice Questions

1. What is the ratio of apples to oranges?

    A. 3 to 4
    B. 4 to 3
    C. 9 to 6
    D. 6 to 9

2. What is the ratio of fish to cats?

    A. 1 to 3
    B. 2 to 1
    C. 9 to 6
    D. 6 to 9

1.1 | Intro to Ratios

3. What is the ratio of cats to dogs?

    A. 3:1

    B. 1:3

    C. 2:7

    D. ~~7:2~~

4. What is the ratio of carrots to ice cream cones?

    A. 2:7

    B. 7:2

    C. ~~5:2~~

    D. 2:5

5. What is the ratio of donuts to candy?

    A. 1:1

    B. 2:1

    C. 1:2

    D. 2:2

AMAZE!!

Use the chart below to answer questions 6 - 10. The chart represents the number of students trying out for each sport.

Sport	Students
Basketball	15
Tennis	14
Soccer	8
Swimming	10
Gymnastics	5
Ballet	7

6. What is the ratio of students trying out for basketball to students trying out for gymnastics?

    A. 3:1
    B. 1:3
    C. 2:1
    D. 2:3

    B 15
    G 5

7. What is the ratio of students trying out for swimming to students trying out for gymnastics?

    A. 1:5
    B. 1:3
    C. 2:1
    D. 2:3

    S 10
    G 5

8. What is the ratio of students trying out for swimming to students trying out for soccer?

    A. 5:4
    B. 4:5
    C. 3:1
    D. 1:3

    S 10
    SS 8

9. What is the ratio of students trying out for soccer to students trying out for tennis?

    A. For every **3** students trying out for soccer, there are **2** students trying out for tennis.

    B. For every **2** students trying out for soccer, there are **3** students trying out for tennis.

O.M.G   **C.** For every **4** students trying out for soccer, there are **7** students trying out for tennis.

    D. For every **7** students trying out for soccer, there are **4** students trying out for tennis.

S 8   T 14
4   7

10. What is the ratio of students trying out for tennis to students trying out for ballet?

    A. For every 2 students trying out for tennis, there is 1 student trying out for ballet.

    B. For every 1 student trying out for tennis, there are 2 students trying out for ballet.

    C. For every 7 students trying out for tennis, there are 2 students trying out for ballet.

    D. For every 2 students trying out for tennis, there are 7 students trying out for ballet.

T 14   B 7

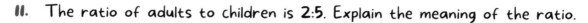

11. The ratio of adults to children is **2:5**. Explain the meaning of the ratio.

   A. There are exactly **2** adults and **5** children.
   B. There are exactly **2** children and **5** adults.
   C. There are **2** adults for every **5** children.
   D. There are **2** children for every **5** adults.

12. The ratio of chocolate chip cookies to total cookies at the bake shop is **9:10**. Explain the meaning of the ratio.

   A. The bake shop has **9** chocolate chip cookies.
   B. The bake shop has **10** chocolate chip cookies.
   C. The bake shop has **1** sugar cookie.
   D. Out of every **10** cookies at the bake shop, **9** are chocolate chip.

13. Write the ratio in its simplest form. For every 1 star, there are | 2 | heart(s).

14. Write the ratio in its simplest form. For every 1 cat, there are _____ dog(s).

3

15. Write the ratio in its simplest form. For every 1 donut, there is ☐ 1 carrot(s).

S   5

Understanding Unit Rates

A **rate** is a specific type of ratio that compares quantities with different units. Examples would be cost per item or distance per time. Consider the problem below.

Sarah can ride her bike **30** miles in **2** hours. If she rides at a consistent rate, how many miles can she ride her bike in 1 hour?

<u>Step 1</u>: Determine the two different units

The two different units are miles and hours.

<u>Step 2</u>: Determine the ratio

The ratio is **30:2**.

<u>Step 3</u>: Find the unit rate

A **unit rate** compares two quantities where one of the terms has a quantity of 1.

To find the unit rate, we need to rewrite the ratio as a division problem. We know that for every **30** miles she rides, Sarah bikes for **2** hours.

This can be written as: $\dfrac{30 \text{ miles}}{2 \text{ hours}}$

Now, we need to simplify the ratio to determine how far she can ride in one hour.

$\dfrac{30 \text{ miles}}{2 \text{ hours}}$ → $\dfrac{15 \text{ miles}}{1 \text{ hours}}$

So, she can ride her bike 15 miles in one hour.

But what if we needed to know how far she could ride in 6 hours?

Now that we know how far she can ride in 1 hour, we simply need to multiply that number to determine how far she can ride her bike in **6 hours.**

$$\frac{15 \times 6}{1 \times 6} = \frac{90}{6}$$

So, she can ride her bike **90** miles in 6 hours. ✓

Practice Questions

1. Baylee drives **264** miles to visit her sister. It takes her **4** hours. If she drove at a consistent rate, how far did she drive in 1 hour?

    A. 42 miles per hour
    B. 66 miles per hour
    C. 88 miles per hour
    D. 132 miles per hour

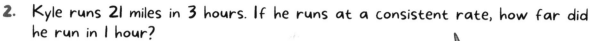

2. Kyle runs **21** miles in **3** hours. If he runs at a consistent rate, how far did he run in **1** hour?

A. 3 miles

B. 7 miles

C. 18 miles

D. 63 miles

3. Amari rides her bike **12** blocks in **2** minutes. If she rides at a consistent rate, how far can she ride her bike in **1** minute?

A. 6 blocks

B. 10 blocks

C. 12 blocks

D. 24 blocks

4. 2 bags of ice cost **$6.00**. If each bag cost the same amount, how much does one bag of ice cost?

A. $0.50

B. $1.00

C. $2.00

D. $3.00

21

5. **6** packs of mints cost **$3.00**. If each pack cost the same amount, how much does one pack of mints cost?

A. $0.50

B. $0.75

C. $1.00

D. $2.00

6. Sofia's car travels **700** miles per **50** gallons of gas. Write a statement to describe the miles per gallon unit rate.

14 miles per gallon

7. A plane flew **874** miles in **2** hours. Write a statement to describe the miles per hour unit rate.

437 mph

8. Lars can swim **100** meters in **10** minutes.
Write a statement to describe the unit rate.

10

9. Olivia can see **45** patients in **5** days. Write
a statement to describe the unit rate.

9

10. The recipe calls for **8** cups of sugar for
every **4** cups of butter. Write a statement
to describe the unit rate.

2 : 1

11. Lara can drive 124 miles in 2 hours. If she drove at a consistent rate, how far could she drive in 5 hours?

62 x 5 = 310

310 miles

12. Kylie can sew 8 dresses in 4 hours. If she sews at a consistent rate, how many dresses could she sew in 8 hours?

16 dresses

13. Liam can write 24 pages of his book in 4 hours. If he writes at a consistent rate, how many pages can he write in 2 hours?

12

14. 4 bags of popcorn cost **$5.00**. If each bag cost the same amount, how much does **3 bags** of popcorn cost?

3.75

5.00 ÷ 4 =
1.25 × 3 = 3.75

× 3 = 2.70

15. At the local bakery, 10 cookies cost **$7.00**. If each cookie cost the same amount, how much would it cost to buy **4 cookies**?

$2.80

7.00 ÷ 10 = 70 ¢

4 × 70 ¢ = 280

10→7
4→2.⁸⁰

$7.00.
COOKIES

by 10 4·   9·

1.3 | Using Ratios to Solve Problems

Using Ratios to Solve Problems

We can use what we know about ratios to find percentages. A percent is simply a rate per 100.

Let's look at an example.

Approximately **8** out of every **25** people are overweight in the United States. What percentage of people are overweight in the U.S.?

To solve the problem, we first need to determine the ratio, which is **8:25**.

Next, we need to determine how many people out of **100** are overweight.

$$\frac{8}{25} = .32 \text{ (Unit Rate)}$$

$$.32 \times 100 = 32\% \text{ (Percent)}$$

We multiply by **100** because a percent represents a rate per **100**.

Approximately **32%** of people are overweight in the United States.

What if the problem asks you to convert a percent to a number?

Taylor has **50** books on her bookshelf. **20%** of the books are nonfiction. How many books are nonfiction?

We need to multiply **20%** by **50**. Remember, percent means per 100. So 20% = $\frac{20}{100}$

$$\frac{20}{100} \times \frac{50}{1} = \frac{10\cancel{00}}{1\cancel{00}} = \frac{10}{1}$$

Taylor has **10** nonfiction books on her bookshelf.

1. The rectangle below represents one whole.
   What percent of the rectangle is shaded? **30%**

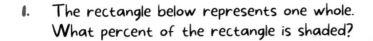

2. The rectangle below represents one whole.
   What percent of the rectangle is shaded? **50%**

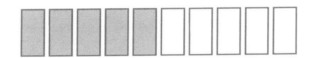

3. The rectangle below represents one whole.
   What percent of the rectangle is shaded? **60%**

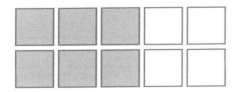

4. The rectangle below represents one whole. What percent of the rectangle is shaded?

5 %

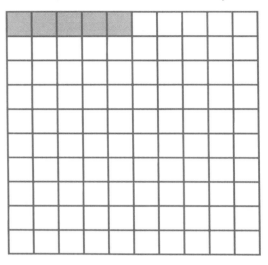

5. The rectangle below represents one whole. What percent of the rectangle is shaded?

30 %

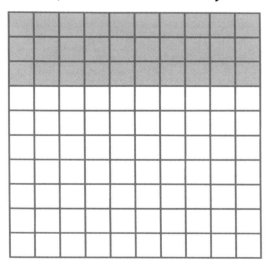

6. **6** out of **20** people said blue was their favorite color. What percentage of people said blue was their favorite color?

30%

7. **8** out of **25** people said vanilla was their favorite flavor of ice cream. What percentage of people said vanilla was their favorite?

32%

8. **5** out of **20** people said basketball was their favorite sport. What percentage of people said basketball was their favorite?

25%

9. **5** out of **50** people had mac and cheese for lunch. What percentage of people had mac and cheese for lunch?

10%

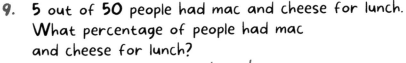

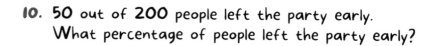

10. **50** out of **200** people left the party early. What percentage of people left the party early?

$$25\%$$

11. Rashkis Middle has **900** students. Approximately **9%** of the students are enrolled in the afterschool program. How many students attend the afterschool program?

$$81$$

12. The library has **876** books. **25%** of the books are informational. How many informational books does the library have?

$$876 \div 4 = 200 + 15 + 4$$

$$219$$

13. The bakery has **35** cakes. **20%** are wedding cakes. How many wedding cakes does the bakery have?

$$7$$

14. The shoe store has **240** pairs of shoes. **40%** of the shoes are women's shoes. How many women's shoes does the store have?

96

15. The middle school has **300** students. **65%** of the students are female. How many females attend the middle school?

190

1. Write the ratio in its simplest form. For every 1 star, there are ___ heart(s).

2. Write the ratio in its simplest form. For every 1 cat, there are ___ dog(s).

3. Write the ratio in its simplest form. For every 1 carrot, there are ___ donut(s).

13

4. The ratio of cats to mice is 3:9. Explain the meaning of the ratio.

   A. There are 3 cats for every 9 mice.
   B. There are 3 mice for every 9 cats.
   C. There are exactly 3 cats and 9 mice.
   D. There are exactly 3 mice and 9 cats.

5. The ratio of cows to total animals on the farm is 6:10. Explain the meaning of the ratio.

   A. The farm has 6 cows.
   B. The farm has 10 cows.
   C. Out of every 10 animals on the farm, 6 are cows.
   D. Out of every 10 animals on the farm, 4 are cows.

14

Use the chart below to answer questions 6 - 10. The chart represents the number of students in each grade.

Grade	Students
Fifth	24
Sixth	20
Seventh	32
Eighth	28

6. What is the ratio of students in fifth grade to students in seventh grade?

A. 3:1 $24 : 32 = 3 : 4$
B. 1:3
C. 3:4 *(circled)*
D. 4:3

7. What is the ratio of students in sixth grade to students in eighth grade?

A. 5:7 *(circled)* $20 : 28 = 5 : 7$
B. 7:5
C. 5:2
D. 2:5

8. What is the ratio of students in fifth grade to students in eighth grade?

$24 : 28 = 6 : 7$

A. 6:7
B. 7:6
C. 3:1
D. 1:3

9. What is the ratio of students in sixth grade to students in seventh grade?

$20 : 32 = 5 : 8$

A. 8:5
B. 5:8
C. 3:1
D. 1:3

10. What is the ratio of students in sixth grade to students in fifth grade?

$20 : 24$

A. 6:5
B. 5:6
C. 5:2
D. 2:5

11. Quinn's car travels **500** miles per **50** gallons of gas. Write a statement to describe the unit rate.

10 mus pr gallon

12. The cookie recipe calls for **3** cups of sugar for every **4** cups of milk. Write a statement to describe the unit rate.

3:4

13. Will can run **24** miles in **4** hours. If he runs at a consistent rate, how far could he run in **6** hours?

36

14. 4 packs of gum cost **$1.00**. If each pack costs the same amount, how much does one pack of gum cost?

25¢

15. Ester can make **15** cakes in **3** days. Write a statement to describe the unit rate.

5 cake per day

16. What is **20%** of **300**?

60

Lobster

18

17. 30 out of **600** students have attached earlobes. What percentage of students have attached earlobes?

5%

18. 50 out of **200** students are wearing flip-flops. What percentage of students are wearing flip-flops?

25%

19. The bakery has **45** cakes. **20%** are birthday cakes. How many birthday cakes does the bakery have?

9

20. There are **200** students in 6th grade. **15%** of the students are at the library. How many students are at the library?

30

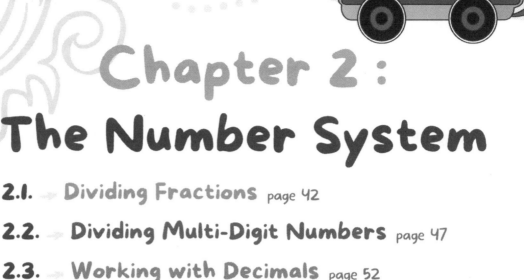

Chapter 2 :
The Number System

ARGOPREP

We can use what we know about multiplication and division to divide fractions by fractions. Most of the time, we can follow a simple formula.

$$\frac{a}{b} \div \frac{c}{d} = \frac{ad}{bc}$$

Let's look at an example.

$$\frac{1}{2} \div \frac{3}{4}$$

Step 1: Turn the second fraction upside down (now it is the reciprocal)

$$\frac{1}{2} \div \frac{4}{3}$$

Step 2: Multiply across the first fraction and the reciprocal

$$\frac{1}{2} \times \frac{4}{3} = \frac{4}{6}$$

Step 3: Simplify the fraction (if needed)

$$\frac{4}{6} = \frac{2}{3}$$

$$\frac{1}{2} \div \frac{3}{4} = \frac{2}{3}$$

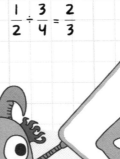

Practice Questions

1. $\frac{5}{8} \div \frac{1}{4} = 2\frac{1}{2}$

   $\frac{5}{8} \times \frac{4}{1} = \frac{20}{8} = 2\frac{1}{2}$

   $\frac{5}{8} \div \frac{1}{4} = \boxed{2\frac{1}{2}}$

2. $\frac{1}{2} \div \frac{1}{8} = 4$

   $\frac{1}{2} \times \frac{8}{1} = \frac{8}{2} = 4$

   $\frac{1}{2} \div \frac{1}{8} = \boxed{4}$

3. $\frac{7}{8} \div \frac{3}{4} = 1\frac{1}{6}$

   $\frac{7}{8} \times \frac{4}{3} = \frac{28 \div}{24 \div} = 1\frac{1}{6}$

   $\frac{7}{8} \div \frac{3}{4} = \boxed{1\frac{1}{6}}$

4. $\frac{2}{5} \div \frac{4}{5} = \frac{1}{2}$

   $\frac{2}{5} \times \frac{5}{4} = \frac{10}{20} = \frac{1}{2}$

   $\frac{2}{5} \div \frac{4}{5} = \boxed{\frac{1}{2}}$

5. $\frac{5}{6} \div \frac{1}{3} = 2\frac{1}{2}$

$\frac{5}{6} \times \frac{3}{1} = \frac{15}{6} = \frac{5}{2}$

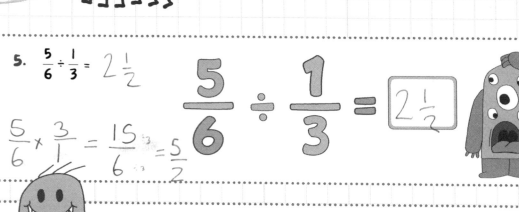

$$\frac{5}{6} \div \frac{1}{3} = \boxed{2\frac{1}{2}}$$

6. How many $\frac{1}{6}$ cup servings are in $\frac{3}{4}$ of a cup of pudding?

$\frac{3}{4} \times \frac{6}{1} = \frac{18}{4} = \frac{9}{2} = 4\frac{1}{2}$

$4\frac{1}{2}$

7. How many $\frac{3}{4}$ miles are in $1\frac{1}{2}$ mile?

$1\frac{1}{2} \div \frac{3}{4} = 2$

8. How many $\frac{1}{8}$ cup servings are in $\frac{3}{4}$ of a cup of punch?

$\frac{3}{4} \times \frac{8}{1} = \frac{24}{4} = \frac{6}{1}$

6

9. How many $\frac{4}{5}$ servings of pie are in $2\frac{1}{2}$ pies?

$$\frac{5}{2} \times \frac{5}{4} = \frac{25}{8}$$

10. How many $\frac{1}{3}$ miles are in $5\frac{1}{2}$ miles? $\left(11\right)$

$$\frac{11}{2} \times \frac{3}{1} = \frac{33}{3} = \frac{11}{1}$$

11. Yolanda has $\frac{1}{2}$ of a cake. How many $\frac{1}{10}$ slices can she cut from it?

$\left(5\right)$

12. Ulysses has $\frac{3}{4}$ of a jug of water. If he uses $\frac{1}{8}$ of the water every hour, how many hours will his water last? Useless $\left(6\right)$ ↓

$$\frac{3}{4} \times \frac{8}{1} = \frac{24}{4} = \frac{6}{1}$$

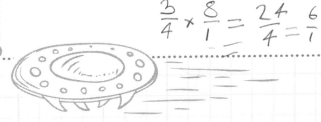

45

13. Ingrid has $7\frac{1}{2}$ pies leftover after her dinner party.
How many guests can she give a $\frac{1}{4}$ slice of pie to? (30)

$$\frac{15}{2} \times \frac{4}{1} = \frac{60}{2}$$

14. Otis has $4\frac{1}{8}$ candy bars leftover from Halloween.
How many friends can he give $\frac{3}{8}$ of a candy bar? 11

240 + 24 = 26

$$\frac{33}{8} \times \frac{8}{3} = \frac{264 \div 8 = 33}{24 \div 8 =} \quad \frac{33}{3} = \frac{11}{1} = 11$$

15. Perri has $4\frac{1}{2}$ carrots. He breaks the carrots into $\frac{1}{4}$ pieces.
How many pieces of carrot does he have? 18

$$\frac{9}{2} \times \frac{4}{1} = \frac{36 \div 2 = 18}{2 - 1 =} = \frac{18}{1} = 18$$

2.2 | Dividing Multi-Digit Numbers

We can use the standard algorithm for division to divide multi-digit numbers.

Let's look at an example.

$$408 \div 12 = \boxed{}$$ Show your work.

We need to determine how many times 12 fits into 408.

```
      3 4
12 | 4 0 8        →   First, we can calculate the number of times 12 fits into 40.
   - 3 6                        40 ÷ 12 = 3 with a remainder of 4
      4 8        →   Next, we calculate the number of times 12 fits into 48
    - 4 8                       48 ÷ 12 = 4 with no remainder
        0                            408 ÷ 12 = 34
```

Sometimes, numbers don't fit evenly into other numbers. In this case, we will have a remainder. For example...

$$408 \div 11 = \boxed{}$$ Show your work

```
      3 7
11 | 4 0 8        →   First, we can calculate the number of times 11 fits into 40.
   - 3 3 ↓                     40 ÷ 11 = 3 with a remainder of 7
      7 8        →   Next, we calculate the number of times 12 fits into 48
    - 7 7                       78 ÷ 11 = 7 with a remainder of 1
        1                            408 ÷ 11 = 37 R1
```

11 does not fit into 1. So we need to express the remainder when we write our answer.

$$408 \div 11 = 37 \text{ R } 1$$

2.2 | Dividing Multi-Digit Numbers

Practice Problems

1. 432 ÷ 12 = 36

$$\begin{array}{r} 36 \\ 12\overline{)432} \\ -36\downarrow \\ \hline 072 \\ 72 \\ \hline 0 \end{array}$$

16 × 5 = 50 30 = 60
16 × 4 = 40 + 29 = 64

2. 720 ÷ 16 =

$$\begin{array}{r} 4 \\ 16\overline{)720} \\ 640 \end{array}$$

$$\begin{array}{r} 3 \\ 96 \\ \times 16 \\ \hline 306 \\ 9\ 60 \\ \hline \end{array}$$

3. 5,494 ÷ 67 =

4. 1,012 ÷ 23 =

48

5. 627 ÷ 33 = [ ]

6. 399 ÷ 19 = [ ]

7. 952 ÷ 17 = [ ]

8. 489 ÷ 11 = [ ] R [ ]

9. 256 ÷ 13 = [   ] R [   ]

10. 856 ÷ 18 = [   ] R [   ]

11. 980 ÷ 45 = [   ] R [   ]

12. 563 ÷ 16 = [   ] R [   ]

13. Principal Puma is planning a field trip for her middle school. There are **540** students total. She can afford to rent **12** buses for the trip. If she splits the students up evenly, how many students will be on each bus?

14. Alyssa needs to reserve tables for a dinner party. There will be **192** guests in all. If each table fits **12** people, how many tables does Alyssa need to reserve for the party if she doesn't want any extra seats?

15. Sujah ordered **468** cupcakes for his wedding. If he sets **26** cupcakes on each table, how many tables will he need to put his cupcakes on?

We can use what we know about standard algorithms to solve problems involving decimals.

Addition	Subtraction
For addition and subtraction, line up the decimals and solve.	

$$2.5 + 1.67 = \boxed{}$$

$$
\begin{array}{r}
2.50 \\
+\ 1.67 \\
\hline
4.17
\end{array}
$$
← You may need to add a zero as a place holder.

Multiplication	Division
For multiplication, calculate the problem as if both decimals were whole numbers. Then, determine where to place the decimal by looking at the place value of the original numbers.	For division, shift the decimals to make the dividend a whole number. Shift the decimal in the divisor the same number of spaces.

Solve: $1.37 \times 2.4 = \boxed{}$

Solve: $15.6 \div 5.2 = \boxed{}$

Step One

$$
\begin{array}{r}
137 \\
\times\ 24 \\
\hline
3288
\end{array}
$$

Step One

$$
\begin{array}{r}
3 \\
52.\overline{)156.} \\
-\ 156 \\
\hline
000
\end{array}
$$

Multiplication	Division
Step Two	
The first number had **2** digits to the right of the decimal. The second number had 1 digit to the right of the decimal. So, that's a total of **3** digits to the right of the decimal. Place your decimal **3** units to the left. 3.288	

Practice Questions

1. 25.7 + 6.24 = 31.94

$$\begin{array}{r} 25.70 \\ 6.24 \\ \hline 31.94 \end{array}$$

2. 45.27 + 17.3 = 62.57

$$\begin{array}{r} 45.27 \\ 17.30 \\ \hline 62.57 \end{array}$$

3. 63.82 + 24.6 = **88.42**

$$
\begin{array}{r}
6\overset{1}{3}.82 \\
24.60 \\
\hline
88.42
\end{array}
$$

4. 2.576 - 1.3 = **1.276**

$$
\begin{array}{r}
2.576 \\
-1.300 \\
\hline
1.276
\end{array}
$$

5. 142.23 - 1.273 = **140.957**

$$
\begin{array}{r}
142.230 \\
-1.273 \\
\hline
140.957
\end{array}
$$

6. 50.071 - 3.45 = **46.621**

$$
\begin{array}{r}
5\overset{4\;9\;10}{0.071} \\
-3.450 \\
\hline
46.621
\end{array}
$$

7. 1.54 × 6.2 = $\boxed{10.58}$

$$\begin{array}{r} {}^2 1\,5\,4 \\ \times\,6\,2\,0 \\ \hline 2\,1\,8\,0 \\ 8\,4\,0 \\ \hline \end{array}$$

8. 12.73 × 5.23 = ☐

9. 43.75 ÷ 3.5 = ☐

10. 3.5 ÷ 1.25 = ☐

We can use what we know about multiplication to find the greatest common factor (GCF) for a set of numbers. For example:

Find the **greatest common factor** of 21 and 7.

To find GCF, we need to look at the factors for each number. Factors are numbers we can multiply together to get other numbers.

21: 1, 3, 7, 21 ⎫ We can see that 21 and 7 have two factors in **common**: 1 and 7.

7: 1, 7 ⎭ Since we are looking for the **greatest** common factor, the answer is 7.

We can also use multiplication to find the **least common multiple (LCM)** of a set of numbers. For example:

Find the **least common multiple** of 3 and 4.

To find the LCM, we need to look at the multiples of both numbers. Multiples are repeated groups of the same amount.

3: 3, 6, 9, 12, 15, 18, 21, 24 ⎫ We can see that 3 and 4 have many multiples in **common**, including 12 and 24.

4: 4, 8, 12, 16, 20, 24 ⎭ Since we are looking for the **least** common multiple, the answer is 12.

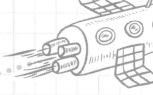

2.4 | Greatest Common Factors & Least Common Multiples

Practice Problem

1. Find the greatest common factor of 10 and 30.

2. Find the greatest common factor of 25 and 50.

3. Find the greatest common factor of 18 and 30.

4. Find the greatest common factor of 16 and 12.

5. Find the greatest common factor of 15 and 45.

6. Find the least common multiple of 5 and 7.

7. Find the least common multiple of 6 and 2.

8. Find the least common multiple of 2 and 9.

9. Find the least common multiple of **8** and **6**.

10. Find the least common multiple of **2** and **10**.

A **rational number** is any number that can be made by dividing two integers. Examples of rational numbers include integers, fractions, and decimals.

Rational numbers include **negative numbers**. Negative numbers are numbers that come before **0** on the number line.

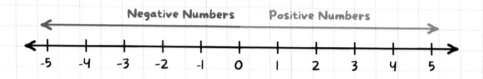

Why would we need negative numbers?

Many measurements, including temperature, elevation, and electric charge use negative numbers. For example:

Stacy checks the weather in the morning. According to her app, it's **-2 °C**. She checks the weather again in the afternoon. The app now says it's **5°C**. Is it warmer or colder in the afternoon?

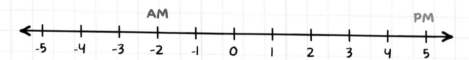

We can see on the number line that **5** is greater than **-2**. What if we want to know how many degrees warmer it is in the afternoon?

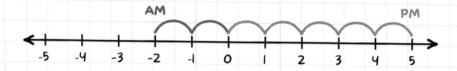

We can count the spaces in between the numbers. We can see that the temperature was **7°C** higher in the afternoon.

2.5 | Intro to Rational Numbers

Practice Questions

1. Fill in the blanks.

-5, -4, [ ], -2, [ ], [ ], 1, 2, [ ], 4, 5

2. Fill in the boxes below.

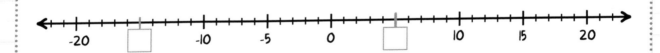

-20   -10   -5   0   10   15   20

3. A business loses $137,000 in March. Which integer represents the loss?

A. 137,000
B. -137,000

4. The students earn **2** hours of free time.
   Which integer represents the time gained?

   A. 2
   B. -2

5. A deep sea diver is **200** ft under sea level.
   Which integer represents the location of the diver?

   A. 200
   B. -200

Use the chart to answer questions 6-10. The chart represents lowest temperatures in different cities during the month of February.

City	° Celsius
Buffalo	-7
Dallas	5
Charlotte	0
Philadelphia	-2

6. Represent the temperatures on the number line below.

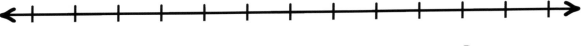

7. What does 0 represent on the number line in question 6?

8. How many degrees warmer is the lowest temperature in Dallas compared to the lowest temperature in Buffalo?

9. How many degrees cooler is the lowest temperature in Philadelphia compared to the lowest temperature in Charlotte?

10. Which city had the coldest day in February?

2.6 | Rational Numbers on a Coordinate Plane

We know that rational numbers appear before and after zero on a number line. The negative sign (-) represents numbers that come before zero. Numbers that come after zero are positive.

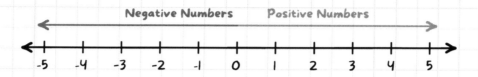

These numbers can also appear on a coordinate plane. A coordinate plane is made up of two number lines: one horizontal number line called the **x-axis** and one vertical number line called the **y-axis**.

We can see that a coordinate plane has negative and positive numbers.

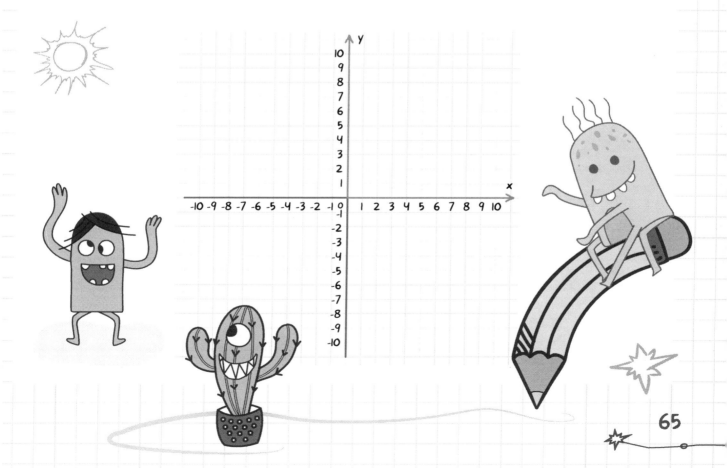

How do you plot negative numbers?

You plot negative numbers the same way you plot positive numbers. You find the number, including the negative sign (-) on the axis. For example

Plot the ordered pairs on a coordinate plane (-2, 2)

To find -2 we travel to the left on the x-axis (before the zero)

To find 2, we travel up on the y-axis (after the zero)

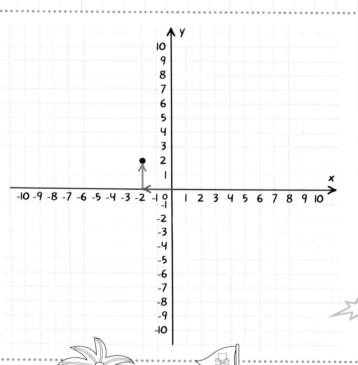

Practice Questions

Use the coordinate plane below for questions 1-5.

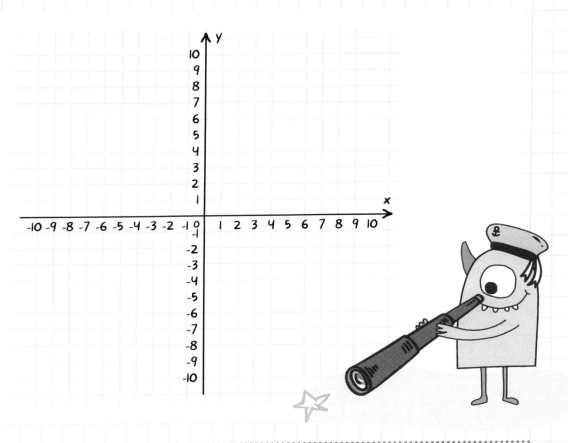

1. Graph and label the coordinates (-3, 4) on the coordinate plane.

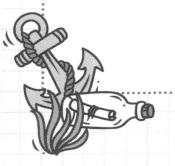

2. Graph and label the coordinates (1, -3) on the coordinate plane.

3. Graph and label the coordinates (2, -4) on the coordinate plane.

4. Graph and label the coordinates (-7, -7) on the coordinate plane.

5. Graph and label the coordinates (5, 0) on the coordinate plane.

Use the coordinate plane below for questions 6 - 10

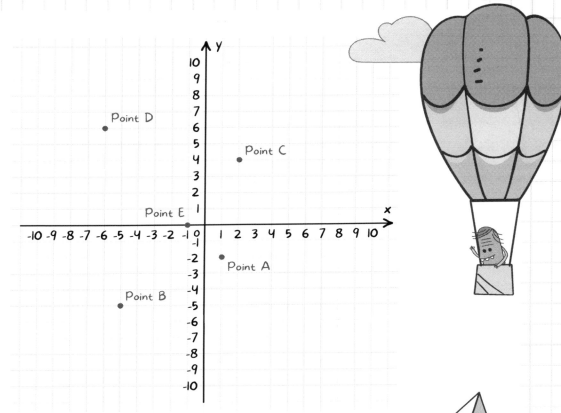

6. What are the coordinates of Point A?

7. What are the coordinates of Point B?

8. What are the coordinates of Point C?

9. What are the coordinates of Point D?

10. What are the coordinates of Point E?

We can use number lines to order numbers and determine absolute value.

An <u>absolute value</u> is a number's distance from 0 on the number line. Absolute value uses the symbol |n|. For example:

$$|\text{-}12| = 12$$

$$|12| = 12$$

-12 and 12 have the same absolute value because they are both 12 spaces from zero on the number line.

Ordering rational numbers is the same as ordering positive numbers. You place them in the order they appear on the number line. For example:

Solve the inequality. -2 ☐ 2

   A. >

   B. <

   C. =

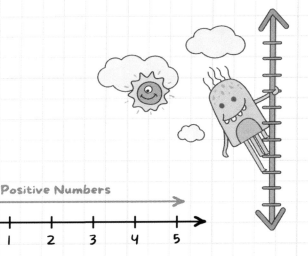

Negative Numbers   Positive Numbers

-5 -4 -3 -2 -1 0 1 2 3 4 5

We can see that -2 is less than 2 because it is farther to the left on the number line. So, the answer is B.

Practice Questions

1. What is $|-1|$?

2. What is $\left|\dfrac{1}{2}\right|$?

3. $|14.5|$ ☐ 14.5

    A. >

    B. <

    C. =

4. $|-5.6|$ ☐ $|5.6|$

    A. >

    B. <

    C. =

5. $|-6|$ ☐ 5

   A. >

   B. <

   C. =

6. $\dfrac{1}{3}$ ☐ $\dfrac{7}{3}$

   A. >

   B. <

   C. =

7. 0 ☐ -5

   A. >

   B. <

   C. =

8. Order the numbers from least to greatest.

   $-9, 2, -\dfrac{1}{2}, 3, 0$

9. Order the numbers from least to greatest.

$-1, \frac{1}{2}, -\frac{1}{4}, 3, 0$

10. Order the numbers from least to greatest.

$|-3|, -2, \frac{1}{2}, 6, 2$

2.8 | Graphing Rational Numbers

We use coordinate planes to help us solve certain math problems involving rational numbers. For example:

What is the distance between (7, -2) and (5, -2)?

The first step is to graph the points on a coordinate plane.

The second step is to count the spaces between the two points.

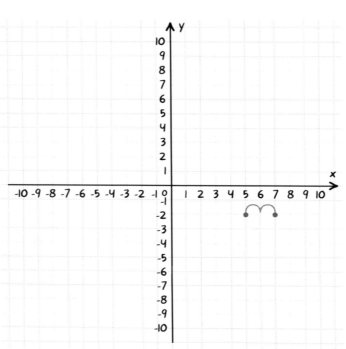

The distance between the two points is **2 units.**

Practice Questions

1. What is the distance between (-2, -3) and (-2, 4)?

2. What is the distance between (5, -2) and (1, -2)?

3. What is the distance between (0, 0) and (0, -6)?

4. What is the distance between (-4, 3) and (-4, -1)?

5. What is the distance between (6, 1) and (6, -2)?

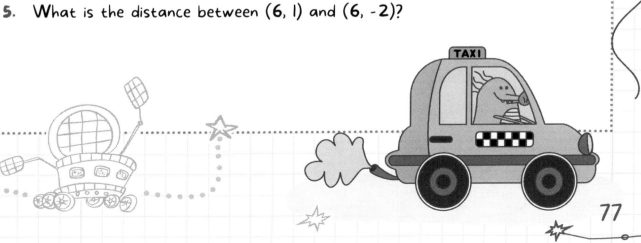

Use the graph for questions 6 - 10. The graph shows a map of George's neighborhood.

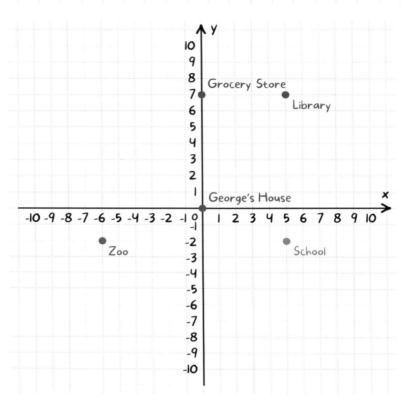

6. The library is located at ([ ] , [ ])

7. The library is [ ] units from the school.

8. The school is located [ ] units from the zoo.

9. George's house is located [ ] units from the grocery store.

10. The grocery store is [ ] units from the y-axis.

1. $\dfrac{1}{4} \div \dfrac{2}{5} =$ ⬚

2. How many $\dfrac{1}{8}$ cup servings are in 8 cups of pudding?

3. John has $\dfrac{7}{8}$ of a jug of water. If he drinks $\dfrac{1}{4}$ of a jug of water every hour, how many hours will his water last?

4. 768 ÷ 12 = [ ]

5. 5,096 ÷ 14 = [ ]

6. Anna needs to reserve tables for a wedding. There will be **264** guests in all. If each table fits **11** people, how many tables does Anna need to reserve for the party if she doesn't want any extra seats?

7. 62.7 + 1.54 = ☐

8. 103.2 + 10.35 = ☐

9. 6.135 – 0.27 = ☐

10. 12.2 – 7.13 = [ ]

11. 15.13 × 3.7 = [ ]

12. 33.6 ÷ 5.6 = [ ]

13. Find the greatest common factor of **8** and **12**.

14. Find the least common multiple of **5** and **7**. Show your work.

15. | -12 | ⬚ 12

    A. >

    B. <

    C. =

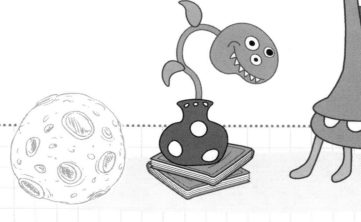

16. |-8| ☐ 3

    A. >

    B. <

    C. =

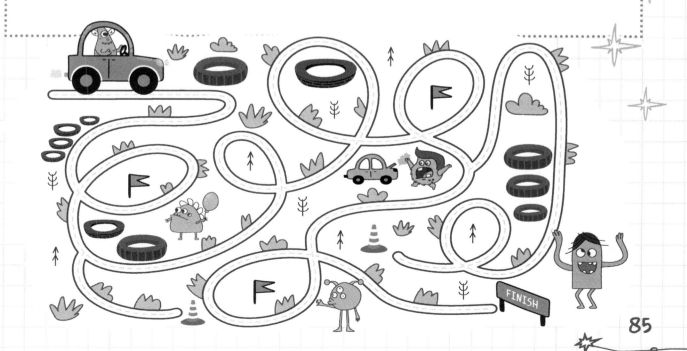

17. Order the numbers from least to greatest.

$6, -2, -\frac{1}{2}, 1, 0$

85

Use the graph below for questions 18 - 20

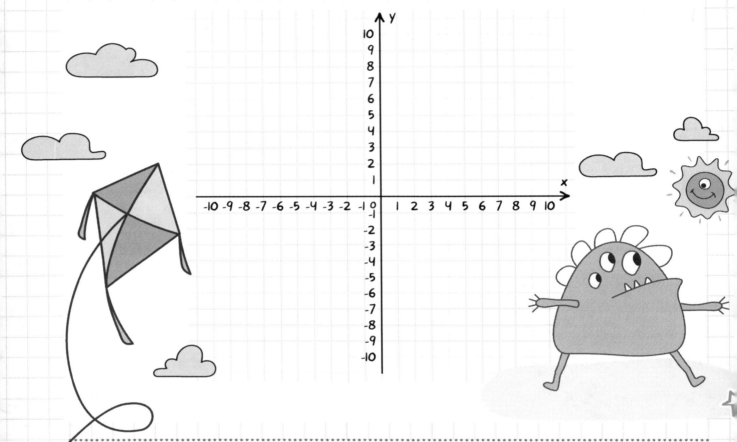

18. Graph and label the coordinates (4, -2) on the coordinate plane.

19. Graph and label the coordinates (4, 2) on the coordinate plane.

20. What is the distance between (4, -2) and (4, 2)?

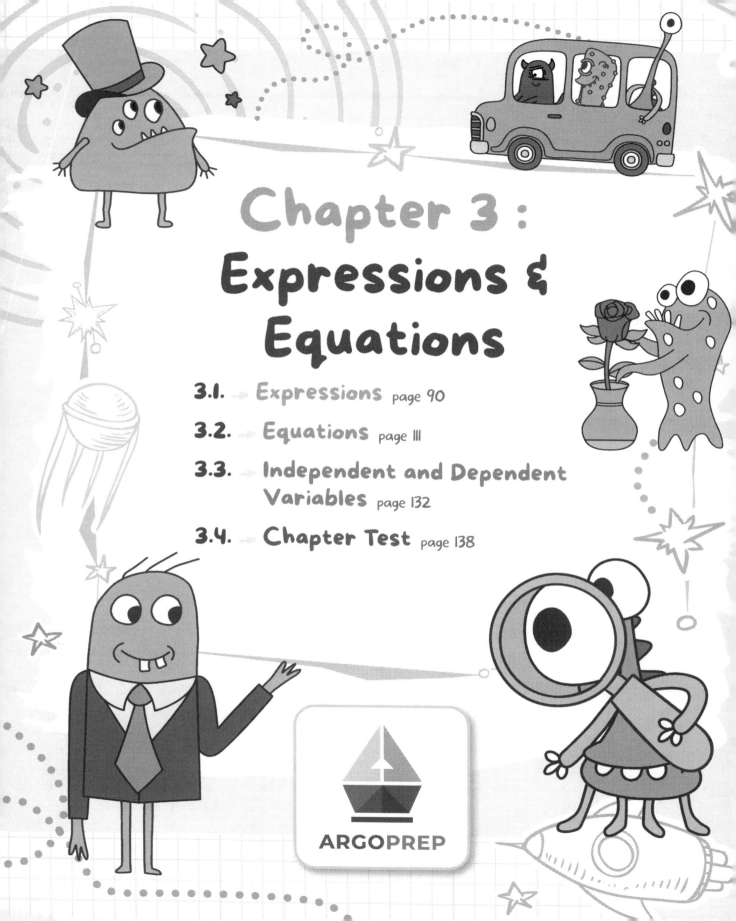

Chapter 3 :
Expressions & Equations

ARGOPREP

We can use what we know about multiplication to write and evaluate expressions involving exponents. For example...

$$3^4 = \boxed{}$$

Let's take a closer look at what the expression is asking us to calculate.

4 is the exponent

3^4

3 is the base number

The **exponent** represents the number of times the base is multiplied by itself. So, in this problem, 3 is multiplied by itself 4 times.

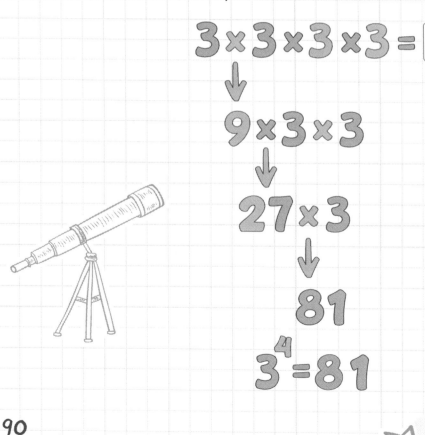

$$3 \times 3 \times 3 \times 3 = \boxed{}$$

$$9 \times 3 \times 3$$

$$27 \times 3$$

$$81$$

$$3^4 = 81$$

Practice Questions

1. $0^3 =$ ☐

2. $6^2 =$ ☐

3. $2^4 =$ ☐

4. $\left(\dfrac{1}{2}\right)^2 =$ ☐

5. 5 x 5 x 5 x 5. Rewrite as an exponential expression.

6. 9 x 9 x 9. Rewrite as an exponential expression.

7. 4 x 4 x 4 x 4 x 4. Rewrite as an exponential expression.

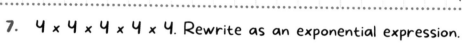

8. 3^3 ☐ 4^2

    A. >

    B. <

    C. =

9. 5^2 ☐ 2^3

    A. >

    B. <

    C. =

10. 4^2 ☐ 6^2

    A. >

    B. <

    C. =

11. $(2 \times 3)^2 + 3 =$ ☐

12. $8 \div (6 - 2)^3 =$ ☐

13. $(5 - 3) + 8^2 = $ ☐

14. $6 \times 2^2 = $ ☐

15. $9^2 - (3 + 6) = $ ☐

In order to write and solve expressions involving letters, we need to first understand variables, terms, and coefficients.

VARIABLES

A variable is a symbol that's used to represent an unknown number

$$3 + 2x = 9$$

x is the variable

TERMS

Terms are single numbers or variables. They can also be a set of numbers and variables that are multipied together

$$3 + 2x = 9$$

There are 3 terms: (3, 2x, and 9)

COEFFICIENTS

Coefficients are numbers placed before a variable when multiplying

$$3 + 2x = 9$$

2 is a coefficient

Let's try using some of the new vocabulary.

The following expression has [ ] coefficient(s), [ ] term(s) and [ ] variable(s).

$$2x - 3$$

[ANSWER] I coefficient, 2 terms, and I variable

95

Now that we understand the vocabulary, we can begin to solve expressions involving variables.

$$\text{Evaluate } 3x - \left(\frac{y}{4}\right) \text{ when } x = 2 \text{ and } y = 8$$

$$3(2) - \frac{(8)}{4}$$

$$\downarrow$$

$$6 - 2 = 4$$

$$\downarrow$$

$$3x - \left(\frac{y}{4}\right) = 4$$

Practice Questions

1. Which expression has exactly 2 variables?

   A. $2(2 + 3) - 3x$
   B. $2x + y$
   C. $2x + 2 = 10$

2. Which expression represents the sum of **3** terms?

   A. 3b + c
   B. (3 + b) + c
   C. 3 + b + c

3. What is the coefficient in the expression 7z + 3?

   A. 7
   B. z
   C. 3

4. How many terms are in the expression xy + cd?

   A. 1
   B. 2
   C. 4

5. Write an expression to represent **5** times *y*.

6. Write an expression to represent the sum of *x* and **3**.

7. Write an expression to represent *x* less than the product of **4** and **6**.

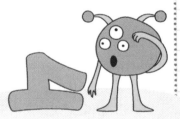

8. Write an expression to represent **12** more than the quotient of *y* and **25**.

9. Write an expression for the problem below.
Kayla read **10** nonfiction books and z fiction books. How many total books did Kayla read?

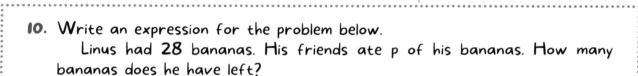

10. Write an expression for the problem below.
Linus had **28** bananas. His friends ate p of his bananas. How many bananas does he have left?

11. Calculate $h^2 - 2x$ when h = 4 and x = 6

12. Calculate $\frac{x}{y} + 3x$ when x = 10 and y = 2

13. Calculate $a^2 + b^2 + c^2$ when a = **3**, b = **5** and c = **2**

14. The baker sells sugar cookies made out of butter and sugar. The number of cookies he bakes is given by **2b + 3s** where b represents the sticks of butter and s represents the cups of sugar.
    How many cookies does the baker make with **6** sticks of butter and **7** cups of sugar?

15. The formula for finding the area of a triangle is $\frac{1}{2}$ x b x h where b represents the base and h represents the height.
    What is the area of a triangle with a base of **10** cm and a height of **3** cm?

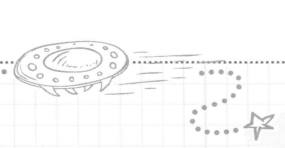

Equivalent expressions are expressions that are written differently but have the same value. Let's look at an example...

Write an expression that is equivalent to **2 (3 + n)**.

We can use our knowledge of multiplication to recognize that **2** times **3 + n** is the same as saying **2** groups of **3 + n**.

We can represent the two groups with a model.

 group 1

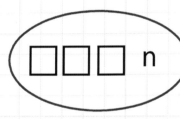 group 2

We can see by looking at the model that the expression could be written as

6 + 2n

We can check our answer with the **distributive property**.

$$2 (3 + n)$$

When using the distributive property, we distribute the **2** to each term within the parenthesis. Doing this allows us to forgo the order of operations, which comes in handy when we are working with variables.

$$2 (3 + n)$$

$$2 (3 + n)$$

$$2 \times 3 + 2 \times n$$

$$6 + 2n \checkmark$$

Practice Questions

1. Use a model to illustrate $4(2 + p)$.

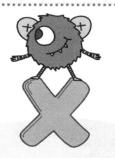

2. Use a model to illustrate $3(x + 4)$.

3. Combine like terms to find an equivalent expression for $2t + 4 + 3t - 2$.

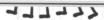

4. Combine like terms to find an equivalent expression for $3y + 2t - t + 2y$.

5. Combine like terms to find an equivalent expression for $4s + 1 - s$.

6. Use the distributive property to write an equivalent expression for $3(7 + n)$.

7. Use the distributive property to write an equivalent expression for $5(2n + y + 3)$.

8. Use the distributive property to write an equivalent expression for $\frac{1}{2}(4x - 6y)$.

9. Factor $50y - 25t$ to find an equivalent expression.

10. Factor $20y - 40$ to find an equivalent expression.

11. Factor $5y - 15t$ to find an equivalent expression.

12. Factor (18n – 9h) to find an equivalent expression.

13. Factor (21 + 3p) to find an equivalent expression.

(21 + 3p)

14. Write **2** equivalent expressions for **2(n + 1)**.

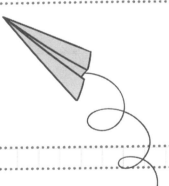

15. Write **2** equivalent expressions for **2c + 6d**.

We can use what we know about writing equivalent expressions to identify when two expressions are equal. For example...

Which expression is equivalent to $z + z$?

A. $2z$
B. z^2

Two expressions are equivalent when they result in the same solution regardless of what number you plug in for the variable.

Let's try plugging in the number **2** to see which answer is equivalent to $z + z$.

$$Z + Z = \underline{}$$

$(2) + (2) = 4$

$2z = \boxed{}$

$2(2) = 4$ ✓

z^2

$(2)^2 = 4$ ✓

Both equations seem equivalent. But let's try when $z = 3$

$z + z = \boxed{}$

$(3) + (3) = 6$

$2z = \boxed{}$

$2(3) = 6$ ✓

z^2

$(3)^2 = 9$ ✗

In order to be equivalent, the expressions must always be equal. Therefore, the answer is A.

$$Z + Z = 2Z$$

Practice Questions

1. Which expression is equivalent to $2x + x + 3y + 2y$?

   A. $2x^2 - 3y^2$
   B. $7xy$
   C. $3x + 5y$

2. Which expression is equivalent to $5 + x + x$?

   A. $5 + 2x$
   B. $5x + x$
   C. $5 + x^2$

3. Which expression is equivalent to $4y + 2y$?

   A. $6y^2$
   B. $2(2y + y)$
   C. $6 + 2y$

4. Which expression is equivalent to $4(x + 3)$?

   A. $4x + 7$
   B. $x + 12$
   C. $4x + 12$

5. Which expression is equivalent to $6(5n + 7y)$?

    A. $30n + 42y$
    B. $6 + 5n + 7y$
    C. $30n + 7y$

6. Which expression is equivalent to $5i - 3 + 2$?

    A. $5(i - 1)$
    B. $5i - 1$
    C. $2i - 1$

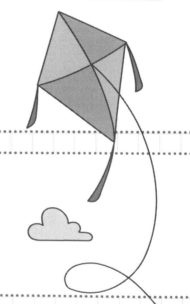

7. Which expression is equivalent to $8(2 - 2g)$?

    A. $16 + 16g$
    B. $16 - 16g$
    C. $8g$

8. True or False. $60 + 15h$ is equivalent to $15(4 + h)$.

9. True or False. 3n - 3 is equivalent to n - 0.

10. True or False. n + n + n is equivalent to n^3.

11. True or False. 3e + 2 - 1 is equivalent to 3e + 1.

12. True or False. 4(3 - t) is equivalent to 12 - 4t.

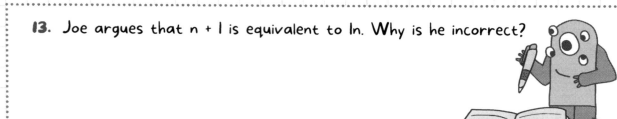

13. Joe argues that n + 1 is equivalent to 1n. Why is he incorrect?

14. Jo argues that $\frac{1}{2}(x - 6)$ is equivalent to $\frac{1}{2}x - 3$. Why is she correct?

15. Georgia argues that p(1 + 2p) is equivalent to 4p. Why is she incorrect?

We can solve one-variable equations and inequalities by plugging in the unknown number. For example...

In which equation does $x = 4$?

A. $2 + x = 4$
B. $2 + x = 6$

Since we know the value of x, we simply need to plug it into each equation to see if it gives us the correct result.

$2 + x = 4$	$2 + x = 6$
$2 + (4) = 6$ ✗	$2 + (4) = 6$ ✓

Choice A is incorrect because we do not get the correct answer when we plug the number in for x.

Choice B is correct because we do get the correct answer when we plug the number in for x.

III

3.2.A | One-Variable Equations

Practice Questions

1. In which equation does x = 4?

    A. $12 - 4x = 11$

    B. $x + 7 = 11$

    C. $\dfrac{22}{x} = 11$

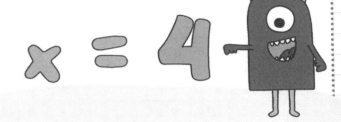

2. In which equation does n = 7

    A. $3n + 4 = 10$

    B. $5n - 4 = 10$

    C. $n + 3 = 10$

3. In which equation does y = 14?

    A. $7 \times 2y = 2$

    B. $\dfrac{y}{7} = 2$

    C. $y + 7 = 10$

4. In which equation does p = 6?

    A. $p - 2 = 4$

    B. $p + 5 = 4$

    C. $p \times 3 = 4$

5. In which equation does w = 9?

   A. $w + 5 = 14$
   B. $w - 5 = 14$
   C. $\frac{w}{4} = 14$

6. In which equation does r = 5?

   A. $3 + r = 6$
   B. $2r - 5 = 5$
   C. $3 - r = 2$

7. In which equation does m = 1?

   A. $2m + 5 = 7$
   B. $m^2 - 1 = 8$
   C. $\frac{m}{4} = \frac{1}{2}$

8. Which number makes the equation $5x = 12 - x$ true?

   A. 1
   B. 2
   C. 3

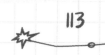

9. Which number makes the inequality 15 > 10n true?

   A. 5
   B. 2
   C. $\frac{1}{2}$

10. Which number makes the inequality 27 < 9 + 2w true?

    A. 6
    B. 9
    C. 12

11. Which number makes the inequality $2 > \frac{n}{2}$ true?

    A. 7
    B. 4
    C. 1

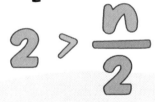

12. Which value makes the equation 12 − w = 3w true?

    A. w = 1
    B. w = 2
    C. w = 3

3.2.A | One-Variable Equations

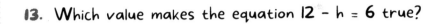

13. Which value makes the equation 12 − h = 6 true?

    A. h = 4

    B. h = 6

    C. h = 8

$$12 - h = 6$$

14. Which value makes the equation 8r × 3 = 48 true?

    A. r = 1

    B. r = 2

    C. r = 3

$$8r \times 3 = 48$$

15. Which value makes the equation $\frac{24}{q} = 12$ true?

    A. q = 2

    B. q = 3

    C. q = 4

$$\frac{24}{q} = 12$$

Variables can represent unknown numbers. We can use what we know about mathematical operations to determine the value of these unknown numbers. For example...

Determine the value of x in the expression $5x = 35$

We can read the expression as **5** times <u>what number</u> equals **35?**

We can use the relationship between multiplication and division to solve for x.

$$5x = 35$$

Divide both sides by **5** to get x by itself.

$$\frac{5x}{5} = \frac{35}{5}$$

$$x = 7$$

We can check our answer by plugging the value back into the original equation.

$$5(7) = 35 \checkmark$$

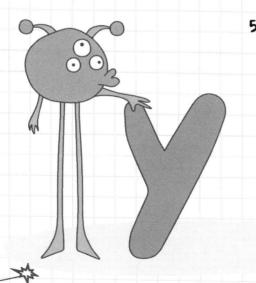

3.2.B | Variables as Unknown Numbers

Practice Questions

1. Determine the value of x in the expression x − 3 = 1.

$$x - 3 = 1$$

2. Determine the value of x in the expression 6x = 60.

$$6x = 60$$

3. Determine the value of x in the expression 2x + 3 = 9.

$$2x + 3 = 9$$
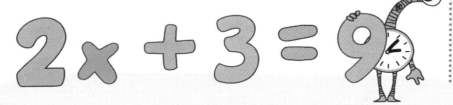

4. Determine the value of x in the expression x ÷ 16 = 2.

$$x \div 16 = 2$$

5. Sarah had 15 pencils when she went to school this morning. She gave x number of pencils away. Now she has 3 pencils left. Write an equation to represent the number of pencils she gave away. Then solve for x.

6. Jet has 27 cups of liquid. 6 of the cups contain lemonade. The rest of the cups contain orange juice. Write an equation using x to represent the number of cups with orange juice. Then solve for x.

7. Henry has 125 oranges divided among x number of baskets. There are 5 oranges in each basket. Write an equation to represent the number of baskets used. Then solve for x.

8. Thea ran a total of 27 miles. She ran 7 miles this morning and x miles this afternoon. Write an equation to represent the number of miles she ran this afternoon. Then solve for x.

9. Baylee wants to buy as many books as possible at the bookstore. She can buy x books for 32.00. Each book cost $8. Write an equation to represent the number of books Baylee can buy. Then solve for x.

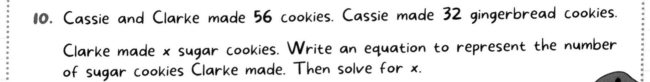

10. Cassie and Clarke made **56** cookies. Cassie made **32** gingerbread cookies.

    Clarke made x sugar cookies. Write an equation to represent the number of sugar cookies Clarke made. Then solve for x.

11. x is **3** times as large as **15**. Solve for x.

12. x is **6** more than **7**. Solve for x.

13. x is half of **22**. Solve for x.

14. **15** is **8** more than x. Solve for x.

15. **24** divided by x is **2**. Solve for x.

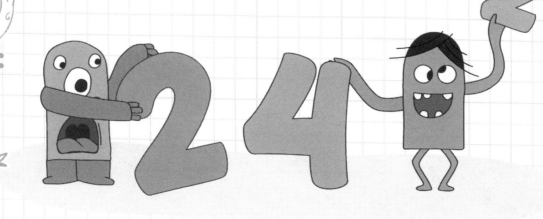

We can use what we know about solving for unknown numbers to rewrite equations involving variables. This can be much simpler than plugging in a set of numbers. For example...

Rewrite the equation $y + 3 = x$ to solve for y

We can use the relationship between addition and subtraction to solve for y.

$$y + 3 = x$$

Move the **3** across the equal sign (=). When we do that, the addition operation changes to subtraction.

$$y + \cancel{3} = x - 3$$

$$y = x - 3$$

Practice Questions

1. Which of the following equations have a value of $x = 2$? Select all that apply.

   A. $x + 3 = 5$
   B. $2x = 6$
   C. $18 - x = 16$

2. Which of the following equations have a value of $x = 3$? Select all that apply.

   A. $3x = 6$
   B. $x + 3 = 6$
   C. $18 - x = 12$

3. Which of the following equations have a value of $x = 5$? Select all that apply.

   A. $5x = 25$
   B. $2x = 10$
   C. $\frac{1}{2}x = 5$

4. Rewrite the equation $2y = x$ to solve for y.

5. Rewrite the equation $5y - 3 = x$ to solve for y.

6. Rewrite the equation $6 \div y = x$ to solve for y.

7. Rewrite the equation $\frac{1}{2} y = x$ to solve for y.

8. Rewrite the equation $3 + 2y = x$ to solve for y.

9. Sarah is **3** times older than Jane. Jane is **2** years younger than Lars. If Lars is 12, how old is Sarah?

10. The baker places chocolate chip and sugar cookies into a box. There are 12 total cookies in the box. There are **2** more chocolate chip cookies than sugar cookies. How many sugar cookies are there?

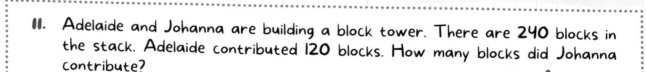

11. Adelaide and Johanna are building a block tower. There are **240** blocks in the stack. Adelaide contributed 120 blocks. How many blocks did Johanna contribute?

12. Lara has enough money, h, to buy **5** carnival tickets. Each ticket cost $3. How many dollars does Lara have to spend?

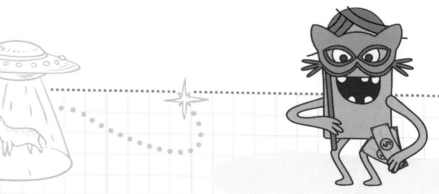

3.2.C | Rewriting Equations with Variables

13. Solve the equation $5 = \dfrac{1}{2}x$.

14. Solve the equation $3 + 5n = 18$.

15. Solve the equation $2.8 = 12.9 - p$.

3.2.D | One-Variable Inequalities

We can use what we've learned about variables to solve inequalities involving unknown numbers. For example...

Create a number line that represents t ≥ 5

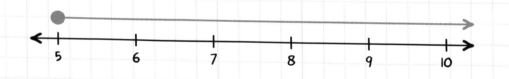

Inequality Signs				
<	≤	=	≥	>
less than	less than or equal to	equal to	greater than or equal to	greater than

We can see that the equation reads t is greater than or equal to 5. So, we need to create a number line starting at 5.

Since t is greater than or equal to 5, we start at 5 and include every number after.

If the equation were t > 5, which reads t is greater than 5, we would not color in the circle above 5.

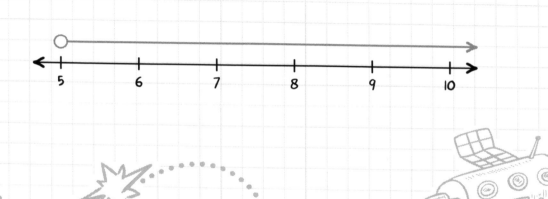

Practice Questions

Create a number line for each expression below.

1. $x > 7$

2. $y \leq 4$

3. $w \leq 6 + 5$

4. $18 \geq p$

5. $-4 < r$

The number lines below represent the value of x. Write an inequality for each one.

6.

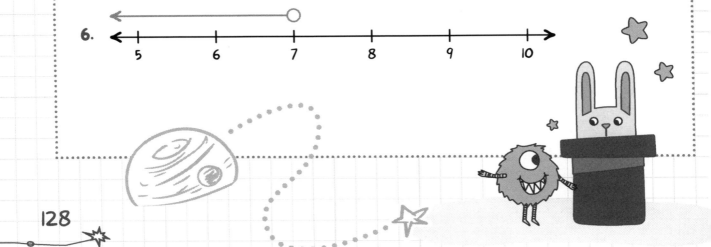

7.

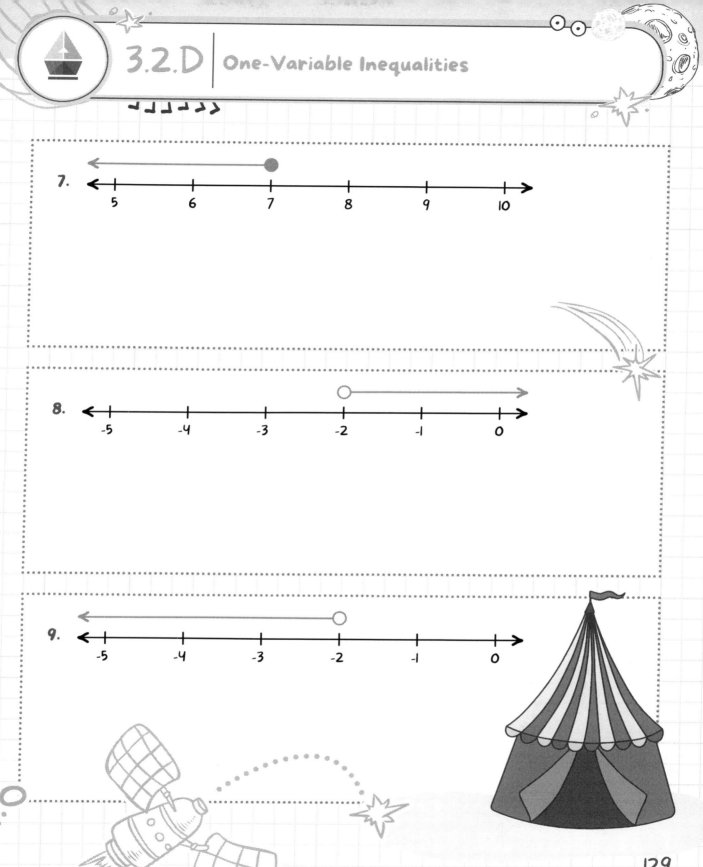

8.

9.

10.

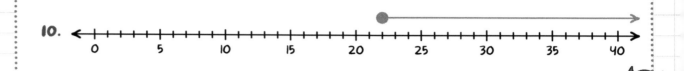

Write an inequality for each situation below. Use x to represent the unknown number.

11. Henry spent more than **$60** on groceries on Monday.

12. Benjamin ate fewer than **23** cookies at the birthday party.

13. In order to win a prize at the carnival, George must knock down at least **5** pins.

14. The students can miss no more than **6** days of school each semester.

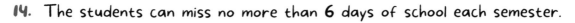

15. Rein must read more than **5** hours each week.

131

3.3 | Independent and Dependent Variables

An independent variable is an unknown number.

A dependent variable is an unknown number that changes depending on the independent variable.

For example...

Sarah always eats **3** times as many cookies as Joey. Write an expression to represent the relationship between the number of cookies Sarah eats and the number of cookies Joey eats. Identify the independent and dependent variables.

We can represent the situation with the expression $s = 3j$

s represents the number of cookies Sarah eats.
j represents the number of cookies Joey eats.

s is the dependent variable because the number of cookies Sarah eats changes depending on the number of cookies Joey eats

$$s = 3j$$

j is the independent variable because it does not change based on other variables in the problem

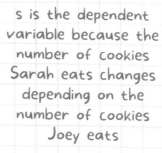

Practice Questions

1. Write an equation for the number of dollars that you spend, s, on lunch if you buy *n* lunches that are $16 each.

2. ⬚ is the independent variable and ⬚ is the dependent variable in question 1.

3. There are f number of flowers in your garden. You planted 13 tulips and s sunflowers. Write an equation to represent the number of flowers in your garden.

4. ⬚ is the independent variable and ⬚ is the dependent variable in question 3.

5. Lena is 3 years older than Sam. Sam is s years old. Write an equation for the Lena's age, l.

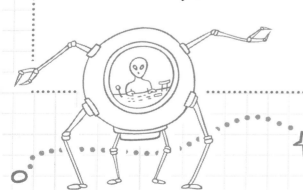

6. ☐ is the independent variable and ☐ is the dependent variable in question 5.

Use the table below to answer questions 7 - 12

$y = 2x + 3$	
x	y
2	
3	
4	

7. Which letter is the dependent variable?

   A. x

   B. y

8. Which letter is the independent variable?

   A. x

   B. y

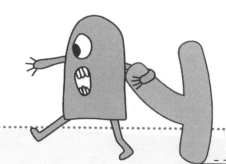

9. Solve for y when x = 2.

10. Solve for y when x = 3.

11. Solve for y when x = 4.

12. When x increases, y [ ].

   A. Increases
   B. Decreases
   C. Stays the same

Use the table below to answer questions 13 – 15

$y = x \div 2$	
x	y
4	
6	
8	

13. Which letter is the dependent variable?

   A. x
   B. y

14. Which letter is the independent variable?

   A. x
   B. y

15. Solve for y in the table. Then graph the points on the coordinate plane below.

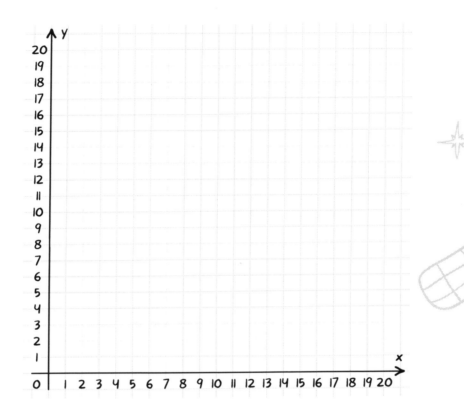

1. $5^3 =$ [ ] .

2. $4^2 =$ [ ] .

3. $3 \times 3 \times 3$. Rewrite as an exponential expression.

4. Which expression has exactly 2 variables?

A. $7x + 3 - 2$
B. $2x$
C. $x + 5y$

5. What is the coefficient in the expression 8 + 9z + t?

    A. t
    B. z
    C. 8
    D. 9

6. How many terms are in the expression y + xz?

    A. 1
    B. 2
    C. 3
    D. 4

7. Which expression is equivalent to 3x - x?

    A. 3
    B. 2x
    C. $2x^2$

8. Which expression is equivalent to $6z + 2 + 3z$?

    A. $9z^2 + 2$

    B. $11z$

    C. $9z + 2$

9. Write an expression to represent 11 less than the product of y and 2.

10. Use the distributive property to write an equivalent expression for $4(x - 3y)$.

11. Factor $16y - 4h$ to find an equivalent expression.

12. Determine the value of x in the expression $6x = 24$.

13. Milo baked 120 cupcakes for the party. She baked c number of cinnamon cupcakes and 64 vanilla cupcakes. Write an equation to represent the number of cinnamon cupcakes Milo baked. Then solve for c.

14. In which equation does $h = 4$?

   A. $2 - h = 1$
   B. $5 + 2h = 13$
   C. $3h = 6$

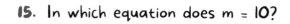

15. In which equation does m = 10?

    A. $2m = 22$

    B. $m^2 - 1 = 99$

    C. $\frac{m}{2} = 6$

16. Kendall and Bowen are skipping rocks. They skip **24** total rocks. Bowen skips half as many rocks as Kendall. How many rocks did Bowen skip?

17. Yolanda has exactly enough money, r, to spend on **3** dresses. Each dress cost $24. How many dollars does Yolanda have to spend on the new dresses?

18. The number line below represents the value of x. Write an inequality for x.

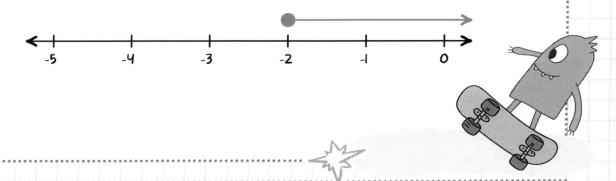

19. Write an equation for the number of cookies you can bake, x, for a party if you have y chocolate chips. You need half as many chocolate chips as the number of cookies.

20. Which variable is the dependent variable in question 19?

A. x

B. y

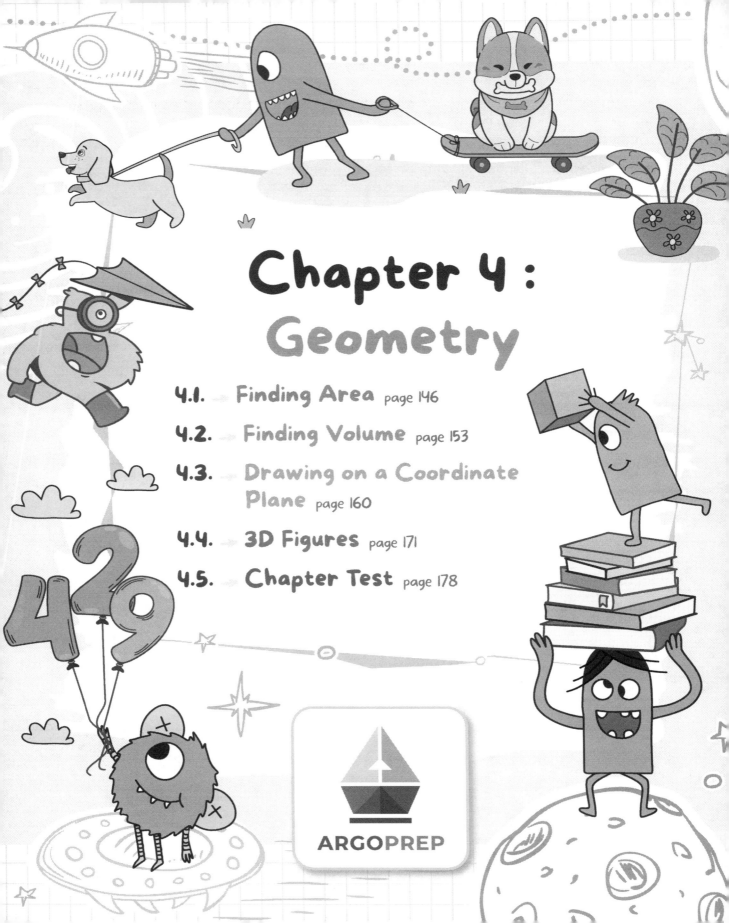

Chapter 4 : Geometry

ARGOPREP

Finding Area

Right Triangles	Rectangles
area = $\left(\dfrac{1}{2}\right)$ (base)(height)	area = (base)(height)
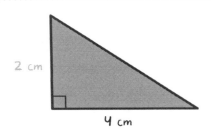	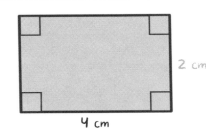
area = $\left(\dfrac{1}{2}\right)$ (4cm)(2cm)	area = (4cm)(2cm)
a = 4 cm²	a = 8 cm²

We can use these formulas to find the area of other shapes as well.

For example...

Find the area of the trapezoid.

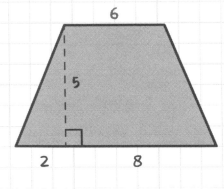

First decompose the shape into **2** triangles and I rectangle.

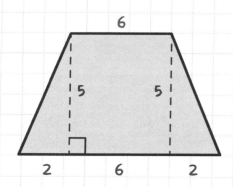

Next find the area of the triangles and the rectangle separately.

Triangle I	Rectangle	Triangle 2
$\frac{1}{2}(2)(5) = 5$	$(6)(5) = 30$	$\frac{1}{2}(2)(5) = 5$

Next, add the areas together.

$$5 + 30 + 5 = 40$$

$$a = 40 \checkmark$$

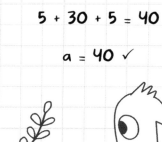

4.1 | Finding Area

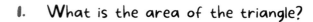

Practice Questions

1. What is the area of the triangle?

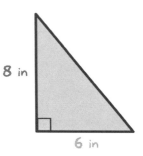

8 in

6 in

2. What is the area of the triangle?

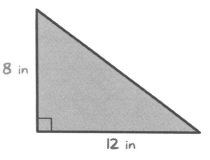

8 in

12 in

3. What is the area of the triangle?

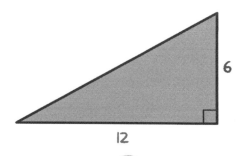

6

12

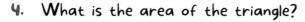

4. What is the area of the triangle?

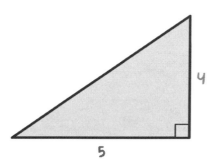

4

5

5. What is the area of the triangle?

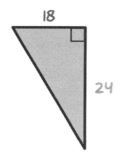

18

24

6. Find the area of the trapezoid below.

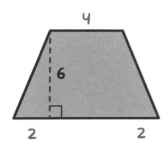

4

6

2   2

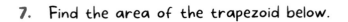

7. Find the area of the trapezoid below.

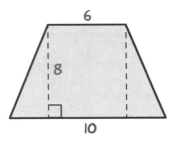

6

8

10

8. Find the area of the trapezoid below.

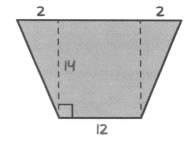

2   2

14

12

9. Find the area of the shape below.

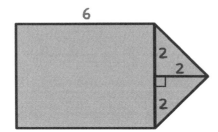

6

2
2

2

10. Find the area of the shape below.

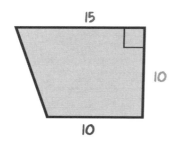

15

10

10

11. A right triangle has an area of **32** cm² and a base of **8** cm. What is the height of the triangle?

12. A right triangle has an area of **4** cm² and a base of **2** cm. What is the height of the triangle?

13. A right triangle has an area of 15 cm² and a height of 6cm. What is the base of the triangle?

14. A right triangle has an area of 30 cm² and a base of 10 cm. What is the height of the triangle?

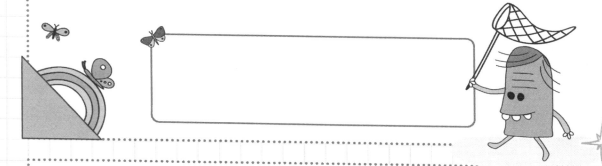

15. A right triangle has an area of 21 cm² and a height of 9 cm. What is the base of the triangle?

There are two different formulas for finding the volume of a rectangular prism.

If we know the height and the area of the base of the rectangular prism, we can use Formula 1.

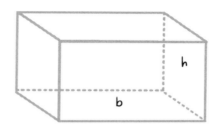

volume = base × height

If we know the length, width, and height of the rectangular prism, then we can use Formula 2.

volume = length × width × height

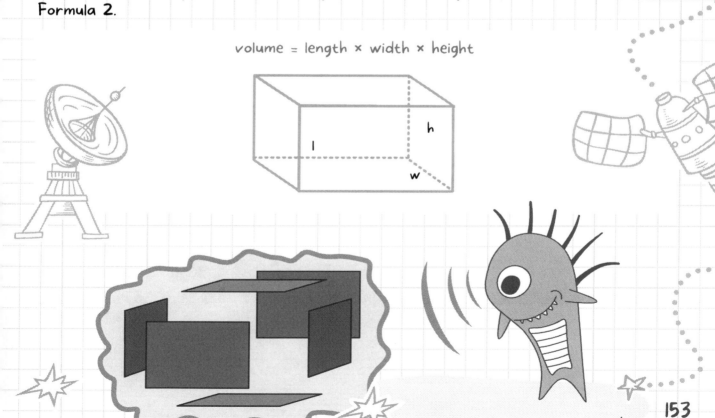

We can use these formulas to determine the volume of rectangular prisms with fractional sides.

For example...

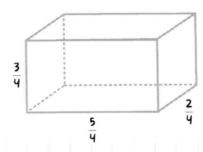

$\frac{3}{4}$

$\frac{2}{4}$

$\frac{5}{4}$

Step 1: Choose a formula

We don't know the area of the base, but we do know the length, width, and height of the rectangular prism. That means we need to use **Formula 2**.

$$\text{volume} = (\text{length})(\text{width})(\text{height})$$

Step 2: Plug & solve

Plug the length, width, and height into the formula and solve

$$\text{volume} = \left(\frac{5}{4}\right)\left(\frac{2}{4}\right)\left(\frac{3}{4}\right)$$

$$v = \frac{30}{64} \text{ cm}^3$$

Step 3: Simplify

If necessary, simplify the solution.

$$v = \frac{15}{32} \text{ cm3}$$

Practice Questions

Use the figures below to answer questions 1 - 5

Figure 1	Figure 2	Figure 3

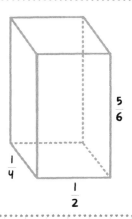

Figure 1: $\frac{5}{6}$, $\frac{1}{4}$, $\frac{1}{2}$

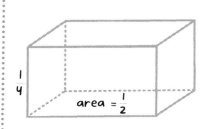

Figure 2: $\frac{1}{4}$, area $= \frac{1}{2}$

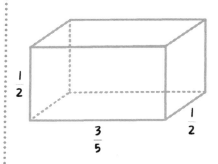

Figure 3: $\frac{1}{2}$, $\frac{3}{5}$, $\frac{1}{2}$

1. What is the volume of Figure 1?

2. What is the volume of Figure 2?

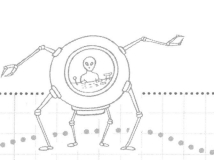

3. What is the volume of Figure 3?

4. Which figure has the largest volume?

5. Which figure has the smallest volume?

6. A rectangular prism has a base area of $\frac{2}{3}$ units² and a height of $\frac{1}{2}$ units. What is its volume?

7. A rectangular prism has a base area of $\frac{5}{6}$ units² and a height of $\frac{1}{2}$ units. What is its volume?

8. A rectangular prism has a base area of $\frac{3}{5}$ units² and a height of $\frac{2}{5}$ units. What is its volume?

9. A rectangular prism has a length of $\frac{1}{8}$ units, a width of $\frac{1}{4}$ units, and a height of $\frac{1}{2}$ units. What is its volume?

10. A rectangular prism has a length of $\frac{3}{4}$ units, a width of $\frac{1}{4}$ units, and height of 1 unit. What is its volume?

11. A rectangular prism has a length of $\frac{7}{8}$ units, a width of $\frac{1}{3}$ units, and a height of **2** units. What is its volume?

12. Mark uses $\frac{1}{4}$ inch cubes to build a tower. The tower is $\frac{3}{4}$ inch wide, $\frac{3}{2}$ inches tall, and **3** inches long. What is the volume of the tower? Use a model to show your thinking.

13. Angela uses $\frac{1}{4}$ inch cubes to build a tower. The tower is $\frac{1}{4}$ inch wide, **1** inch tall, and $3\frac{1}{2}$ inches long. What is the volume of the tower? Use a model to show your thinking.

14. Luna bought a rectangular aquarium with an **8 ft²** base. The aquarium is $4\frac{1}{2}$ ft tall. What is its volume? Use a model to show your thinking.

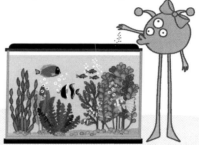

15. Harry is wrapping his brother's birthday present. The base of the present is **5 ft²**. The height of the package is $\frac{5}{2}$ ft. What is the volume of the present? Use a model to show your thinking.

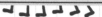

Drawing on a Coordinate Plane

A coordinate plane can help you examine the different properties of a shape. For example...

The rectangle ABCD has vertices at A(-6, 0), B(1, 0), C(1, 3) and D(-6, 3). What is the area of the rectangle?

Step 1: Draw the Shape

Use the coordinates to graph the rectangle on the coordinate plane.

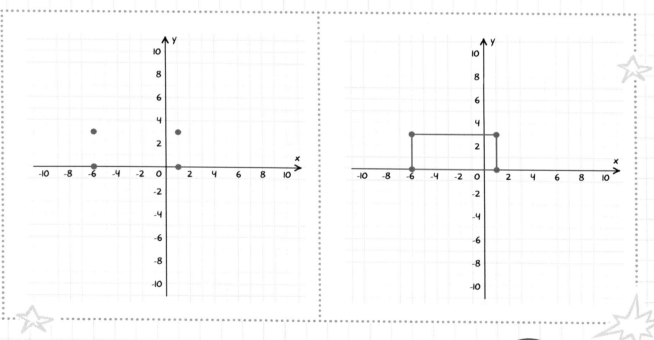

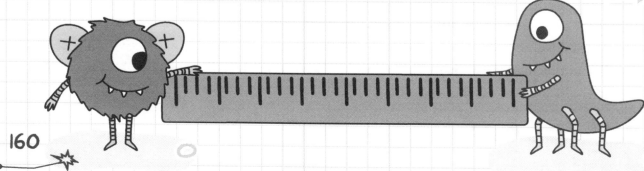

Step 2: Determine the area

The formula for finding the area of a rectangle is a = (length)(width). We can determine the length and width by counting the units on the graph.

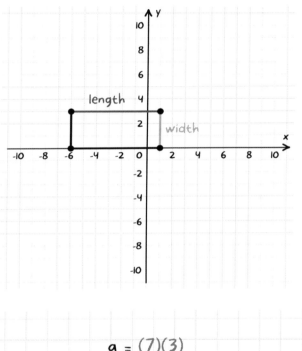

$$a = (7)(3)$$

area = **21** units

Step 3: Check your answer

You can check your answer by counting the units within the rectangle.

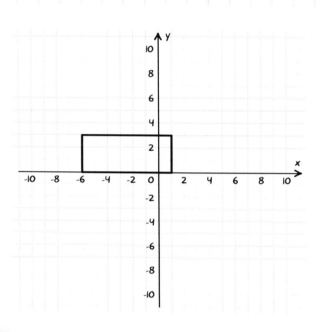

area = 21 units ✓

We can use the same graph to find the perimeter of the rectangle.

perimeter = 2(length + width)

p = 2(7 + 3)

p = 20

162

Practice Questions

Use the coordinate plane to answer questions 1-4

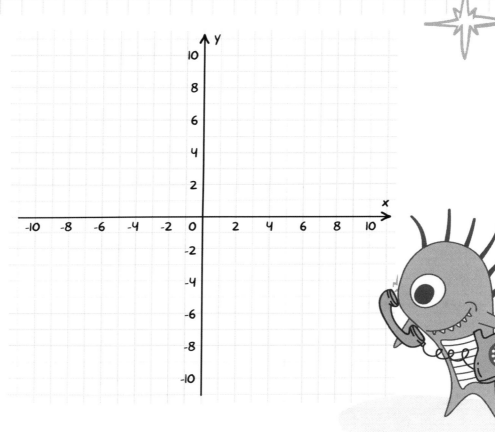

1. Draw a rectangle with vertices at A (0, 0), B (4, 0), C (4, 4) and D (0, 4)

2. What is the length of the rectangle?

3. What is the width of the rectangle?

4. What is the area of the rectangle?

Use the coordinate plane to answer questions 5 - 7

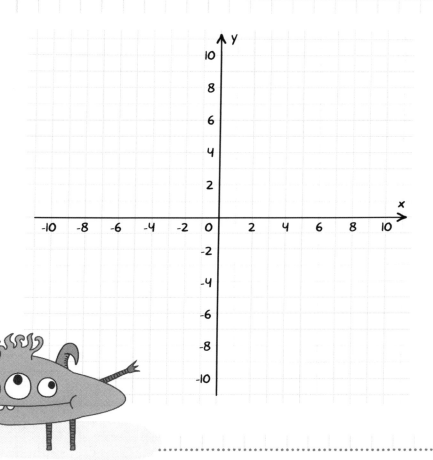

5. Draw a rectangle with vertices at A(-8, 4), B(0, 4), C(0, 8) and D(-8, 8)

6. What is the area of the rectangle?

7. What is the perimeter of the rectangle?

Use the coordinate plane to answer questions 8 - 11

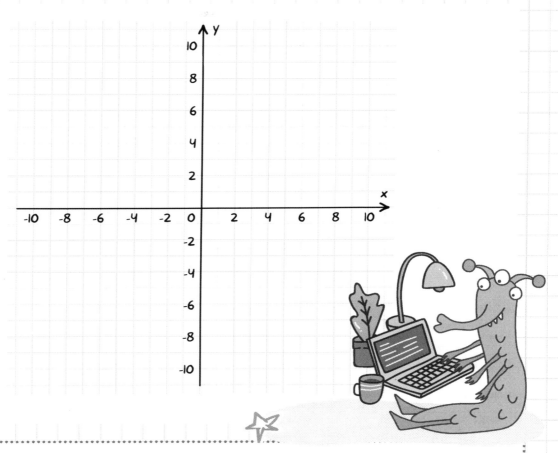

8. Draw a triangle with vertices at A(2, 0), B(-2, 0) and C(0, 5).

9. What is the length of side AB?

10. What is the height of the triangle?

11. What is the area of the triangle?

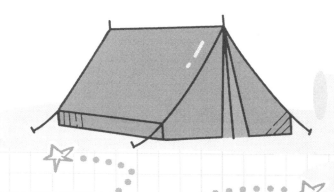

Use the coordinate plane to answer questions 12 - 15

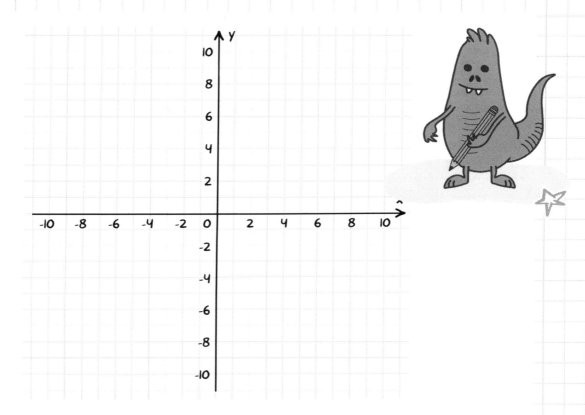

12. Draw a triangle with vertices at A(0, 0), B(6, 2) and C(0, 2).

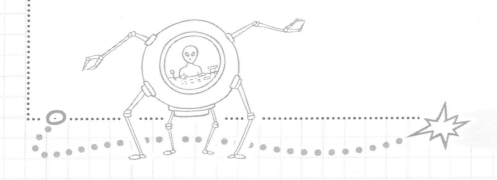

13. What is the length of side AC?

14. What is the height of the triangle?

15. What is the area of the triangle?

4.4 | 3D Figures

We can represent three-dimensional figures on coordinate planes using nets. Nets are made up of rectangles and triangles. They help us calculate surface area.

For example...

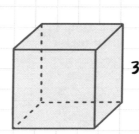

3

We can draw the cube as a two-dimensional shape using graph paper. Draw the shape as if it were lying flat and open.

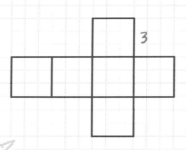

3

Find the area of each part of the shape. Then add all of the areas together.

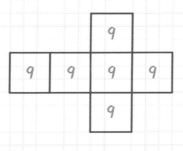

9

9 9 9 9

9

For this example, each shape is a square. The formula for finding the area of a square is area = (side)^2. However, by using graph paper, we can simply count the units in each square.

$$9 + 9 + 9 + 9 + 9 + 9 = 54$$

or

$$9(6) = 54$$

The surface area of the cube is 54 units^3

Practice Questions

1. What is the surface area for the cube represented by the net below?

2. Find the surface area of the cube below using its net. Hint: Squared units are always used to represent area.

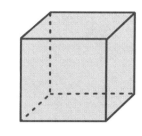 **5** units²

3. Find the surface area of the cube below using its net.

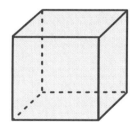 **2** units²

4. Find the surface area of the cube below using its net.

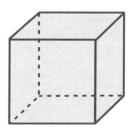 **4** units²

5. What is the surface area for the pyramid represented by the net below?

6. Find the surface area of the pyramid below using its net.

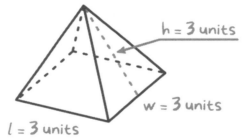

h = 3 units

w = 3 units

l = 3 units

7. Find the surface area of the pyramid below using its net.

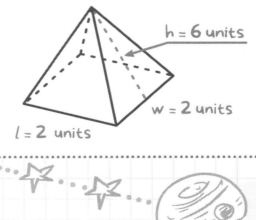

h = 6 units

w = 2 units

l = 2 units

8. Find the surface area of the pyramid below using its net.

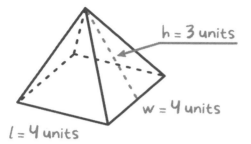

h = 3 units

w = 4 units

l = 4 units

9. What is the surface area for the rectangular prism represented by the net below?

10. Find the surface area of the rectangular prism below using its net.

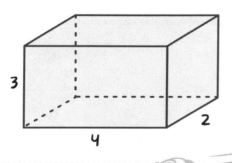

3

2

4

11. Find the surface area of the rectangular prism below using its net.

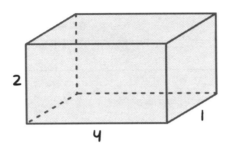

2

4

1

12. Find the surface area of the rectangular prism below using its net.

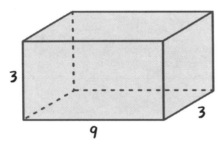

3

9

3

13. Dan is wrapping a present in a rectangular box. The base of the box is 4 ft wide and 2 ft long. The height of the box is 5 ft tall. How many square feet of wrapping paper does Dan need to cover the gift box?

4.4 | 3D Figures

14. Canyon is wrapping a present in a box that is **6** inches long , **4** inches tall, and **4** inches wide. How many square inches of wrapping paper does he need to cover the surface of the box?

15. Sarah needs to cover a cube in foil for her science project. One side of the cube is **3** inches². How much foil does she need to cover the cube?

1. What is the area of the triangle?

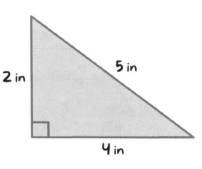

2 in
5 in
4 in

2. A right triangle has an area of 9 cm² and a base of 9 cm. What is the height of the triangle?

3. A right triangle has an area of 14 cm² and a height of 7 cm. What is the base of the triangle?

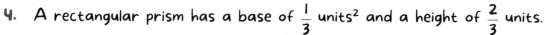

4. A rectangular prism has a base of $\frac{1}{3}$ units² and a height of $\frac{2}{3}$ units. What is its volume?

5. A rectangular prism has a base of $\frac{1}{6}$ units² and a height of $\frac{3}{5}$ units. What is its volume?

6. Layla uses $\frac{1}{2}$ inch cubes to build a tower. The tower is 2 inches wide, $\frac{3}{2}$ inches tall, and $3\frac{1}{2}$ inches long. What is the volume of the tower? Use a model to show your thinking.

Use the coordinate plane to answer questions 7 - 10

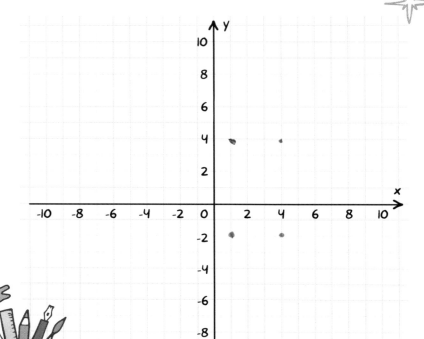

7. Draw a rectangle with vertices at A(1, -2), B(1, 4), C(4, -2) and D(4, 4).

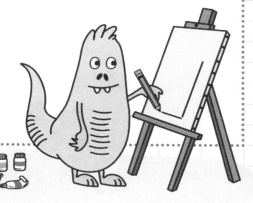

8. What is the length of the rectangle?

6

9. What is the width of the rectangle?

3

10. What is the area of the rectangle?

18

Use the coordinate plane to answer questions 11 – 14

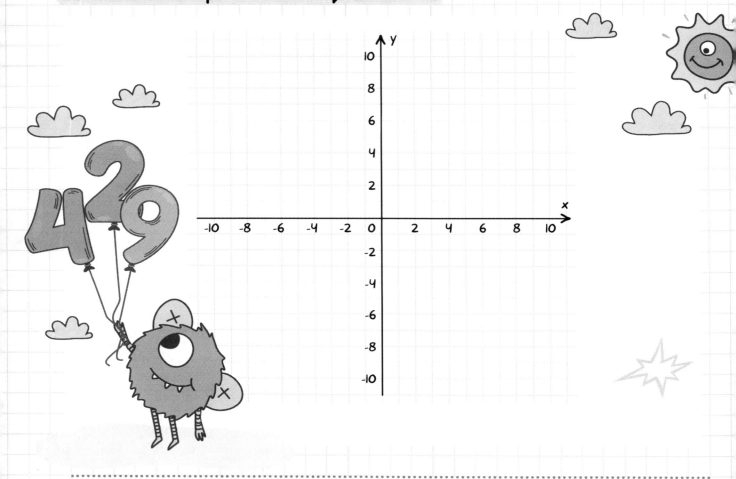

11. Draw a triangle with vertices at A(-4, 0), B(-4, -3) and C(-2, -3).

12. What is the height of the triangle?

13. What is the length of the triangle?

14. What is the area of the triangle?

15. Draw a net to find the surface area of the cube below.

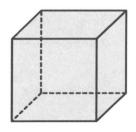

1 units²

Chapter 5 :
Statistics & Probability

ARGOPREP

We can use what we know about collecting data to answer **statistical questions**. Statistical questions anticipate **variability** in the data collected, which means that the answers to the question will not all be the same.

For example...

The question How fast did the students in my class run the race? is statistical because you need to collect data in order to answer it AND there is variability in the data.

Data Collected ✓   Variability ✓

each students race time   different finish times

The question How fast did Frank run the race? is not statistical because it only has one answer.

Data Collected ✓   Variability ✗

Frank's race time   only one answer - no variability

Practice Problems

Determine whether questions 1-10 are statistical or not statistical.

1. How many pizzas did the pizzeria bake?

   A. Statistical   **B.** Not Statistical

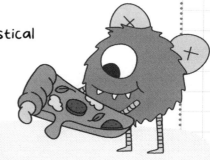

2. How many pizzas does the pizzeria sell each day in the month of August?

   A. Statistical   **B.** Not Statistical

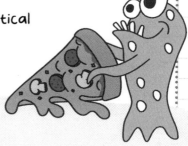

3. How many cookies do middle school students typically eat in one week?

   A. Statistical   **B.** Not Statistical

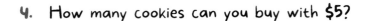

4. How many cookies can you buy with $5?

   A. Statistical   **B.** Not Statistical

5. How many students like blue more than red?

   A. Statistical   **B.** Not Statistical

6. Does Jet like blue more than red?

   A. Statistical   **B.** Not Statistical

7. How tall are most sixth graders?

   A. Statistical   **B.** Not Statistical

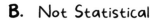

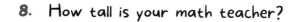

8. How tall is your math teacher?

    A. Statistical   **B.** Not Statistical

9. How many books did you read last summer?

    A. Statistical   **B.** Not Statistical

10. Which book was borrowed from the library the most last summer?

    A. Statistical   **B.** Not Statistical

11. Tina coaches middle school basketball. During the games, she records the number of baskets each player makes and the number of baskets each player misses. Create two statistical questions that could be answered using the data Tina collected.

12. Kendra and her friends created a bar graph representing their favorite songs. Create two statistical questions that could be answered using the data Kendra collected.

13. Francis recorded each student's favorite subject in school. Create two statistical questions that could be answered using the data Francis collected.

14. Paul weighed and measured all of the rocks in his collection. Create two statistical questions that could be answered using the data Paul collected.

15. Nolan kept a journal of birds he saw while bird watching last spring. He recorded their color and size. Create two statistical questions that could be answered using the data Nolan collected.

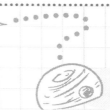

Statistical data has a **distribution**. The distribution gives us a better
of the data collected.

For example...

The graph below shows the distribution of science exam scores for Mr. Walker's
class. What information can you determine based on the data collected?

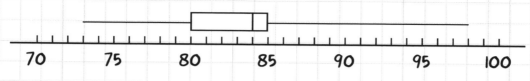

The graph shows us the spread, center and median.

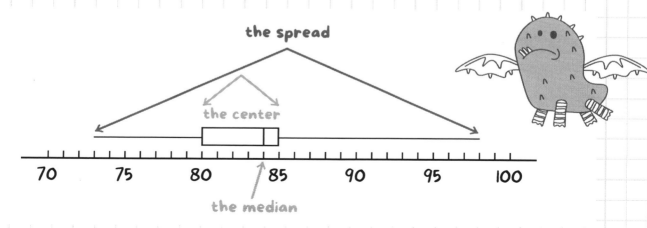

The **spread** is the range of data points, from least to greatest. In this example, the
spread is from **73 - 98**.

The center is a range of points where most of the data occurs. In this example, the
center is represented by a rectangular box. The center ranges from **80 - 85**. So,
most people in Mr. Walker's class scored between an **80** and **85** on the science test.

The **median** represents the midpoint of the data. In this example, the median is **84**.

...another example...

...nformation does the line plot give us about the distribution of data?

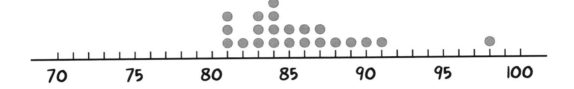

The line plot shows us the shape of the distribution. It also shows us if there are any outliers.

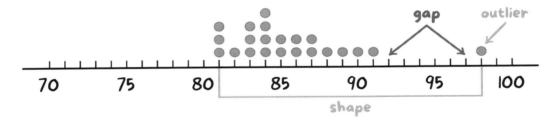

The **shape** can be symmetrical, meaning it's even on both sides of the center. It can also be left-tailed or right-tailed. This example is right-tailed because the data thins out to the right, making it look like it has a tail.

An **outlier** is one point that is far away from the rest of the data points. In this example, 98 is an outlier because there are no other points near it.

A **gap** is a large space between two data points. In this example, there is a gap between 91 - 98.

Practice Questions

The box plot below shows the number of laps the students in Ms. Gamble's class ran during gym class. Use the graph to answer questions 1-5.

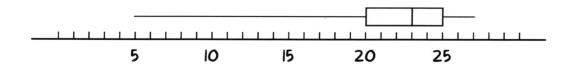

1. The distribution is ⬚.

    A. Symmetrical
    B. Left-tailed
    C. Right-tailed

2. The center of the distribution is ⬚ laps.

    A. 5 - 27
    B. 5 - 30
    C. 20 - 23
    D. 20 - 25

193

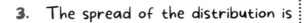

3. The spread of the distribution is [   ] laps.

   A. 5 - 27
   B. 5 - 30
   C. 20 - 23
   D. 20 - 25

4. What is the data's median value?

   A. 5
   B. 20
   C. 23
   D. 25

5. What else can you determine from the graph?

5.1.B | Statistical Distribution

The line plot below shows the number of school days missed by the students in Mrs. O'Dor's class. Use the graph to answer questions 6-10.

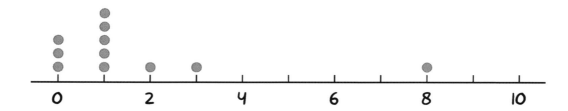

6. The distribution has [ ].

   A. a gap
   B. an outlier
   C. all of the above

7. The distribution is [ ].

   A. symmetrical
   B. left-tailed
   C. right-tailed

8. The center of the distribution is [____].

A. 1
B. 2
C. 3

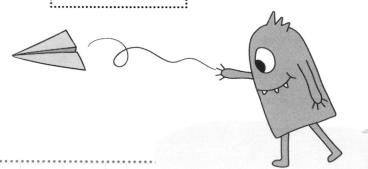

9. The spread of the distribution is [____].

A. 0 - 1
B. 0 - 8
C. 3 - 8

10. How many days of school did most students in Mrs. O'Dor's class miss?

A. 0
B. 1
C. 2

The box plot below represents test scores for the students in Mrs. Greer's class. Use the graph to answer questions 11 - 15.

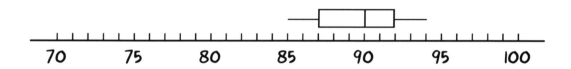

11. The distribution is [ ].

   A. symmetrical
   B. left-tailed
   C. right-tailed

12. The center of the distribution is [ ].

   A. 85 - 94
   B. 87 - 92
   C. 90 - 92
   D. 92 - 94

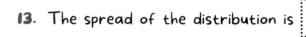

13. The spread of the distribution is [   ].

    A. 85 - 94
    B. 87 - 92
    C. 90 - 92
    D. 92 - 94

14. The median test score was [   ].

    A. 85
    B. 87
    C. 90
    D. 92

15. Which choice shows a data set that could be represented by the box plot?

    A. 83, 85, 90, 90, 94
    B. 85, 86, 86, 90, 97
    C. 85, 86, 90, 90, 94

The **center** of a numerical data set summarizes all of the values with one number. Mathematicians often use *mean* or *median* to calculate the center of their data set.

Mean

The mean is the average.

Add all of the numbers in a data set and then divide the sum by the total number of data points.

data set: **6, 8, 6, 8, 7, 4, 3**

$6 + 8 + 6 + 8 + 7 + 4 + 3 = 42$

$42 \div 7 = 6$

mean = **6**

Median

The median is the middle value.

Order the numbers in a data set from least to greatest. Identify the number that falls in the middle.

data set: **6, 8, 6, 8, 7, 4, 3**

3, 4, 6, 6, 7, 8, 8

median = **6**

The **variation** uses one number to describe how all of the values are different. The most basic measure of variation is *range*.

Range

The range is the difference between the highest and lowest value in a data set.

Subtract the lowest value from the highest value.

6, 8, 6, 8, 7, 4, 3

$8 - 3 = 5$

range = **5**

199

Practice Questions

1. Which data set has a range of 5?

    A. 1, 2, 3, 4, 5
    B. 0, 1, 2, 3, 4, 5
    C. 5, 10, 15, 20, 25

2. Which data set has a range of 15?

    A. 6, 4, 15, 18, 3
    B. 6, 4, 15, 18, 2
    C. 6, 4, 15, 18, 1

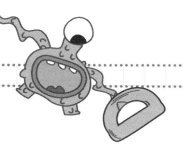

3. Which data set has a mean of 7?

    A. 4, 8, 7, 6
    B. 3, 7, 7, 6
    C. 3, 8, 11, 6

4. Which data set has a mean of 5?

    A. 7, 7, 8, 9, 10, 2
    B. 7, 3, 9, 5, 2, 4
    C. 7, 7, 8, 9, 13, 2

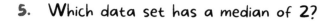

5. Which data set has a median of 2?

    A. -1, 4, -3, 5, 2
    B. -1, -4, -3, 5, 2
    C. -1, 4, -3, -5, 2

Use the data set below to answer questions 6 - 8

76, 98, 82, 97, 90, 93, 94

6. Use range to determine the variation of the data set.

7. Use mean to determine the center of the data set.

8. Use median to determine the center of the data set.

Use the data set below to answer questions 9 - 11

75, 56, 77, 82, 90

9. Use range to determine the variation of the data set.

10. Use median to determine the center of the data set.

11. Use mean to determine the center of the data set.

5.1.C | Statistical Variation

Use the data set below to answer questions 12 - 15

90, 92, 96, 95, 92

12. Use range to determine the variation of the data set.

13. Use median to determine the center of the data set.

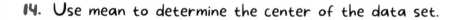

14. Use mean to determine the center of the data set.

15. Why are the mean and median different?

5.2.A | Displaying Statistical Data

There are many ways to display statistical data. We already know how to create number plots and histograms. **Box plots** are another common way to plot data sets.

We can use what we know about analyzing box plots to create our own graphs.

For example...

Use a box plot to display the data set: 81, 73, 80, 82, 84, 84, 84, 85, 85

Step 1: Determine IQR

Start with the Interquartile Range (IQR). The interquartile range is the range of center points. There are five steps for calculating IQR.

1. Order the data from least to greatest

$$73, 80, 81, 82, 84, 84, 84, 85, 85$$

2. Find the median

$$\cancel{73, 80, 81, 82,} 84, \cancel{84, 84, 85, 85}$$

3. Calculate the median of the lower half of the data

$$\cancel{73,} 80, 81, 82 \longrightarrow 80 + 81 = \frac{161}{2} = 80.5$$

4. Calculate the median of the upper half of the data

$$84, 84, 85, 85 \longrightarrow \frac{84 + 85}{2} = 84.5$$

5. Calculate the difference between the upper and lower median.

$$84.5 - 80.5 = \underline{4}$$

Step 2: Draw the IQR

Now that we've determined the IQR, we can begin drawing our box plot. We start with the IQR that we just calculated. We use a rectangle to represent IQR. According to our calculations, we should start at 80.5 and end at 84.5.

Step 3: Draw the Spread

The spread is the range of data points, from least to greatest. In this example, the spread is from 73 - 85. We represent the spread with a horizontal line.

Step 4: Draw the Center

The center is calculated using median. We know the median is 84 from when we calculated the IQR. We use a horizontal line to represent it on the box plot.

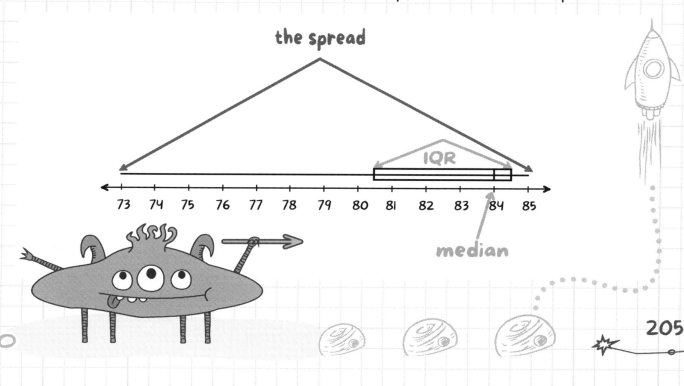

Practice Questions

The data below shows the number of days it rained each month in New York in 2018. Use the data set to answer questions 1-3.

11, 9, 12, 11, 11, 10, 11, 10, 8, 9, 9, 10

1. Use range to determine the variation of the data set.

2. Use median to determine the center of the data set.

3. Draw a box plot to represent the data.

5.2.A | Displaying Statistical Data

The data below shows test scores for Mrs. Pegram's class. Use the data set to answer questions 4 - 7.

56, 78, 85, 86, 87, 87, 92

4. Use range to determine the variation of the data set.

5. Use median to determine the center of the data set.

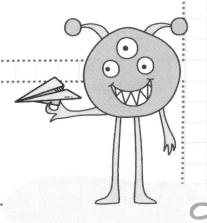

6. Draw a histogram to represent the data.

7. How is a histogram different from a box plot?

The data below shows the number of miles each student ran on field day. Use the data set to answer questions 8 - 11.

1, 2, 3, 2, 1, 5, 2, 1, 2, 3

8. Use range to determine the variation of the data set.

9. Use mean to determine the center of the data set.

10. Draw a line plot to represent the data.

11. What information does a line plot provide that a box plot does not?

12. Draw a box plot and line plot for the data 7, 8, 9, 9, 12.

13. How do the two graphs in question 12 differ?

14. Draw a box plot and line for the data 19, 26, 27, 28, 31.

15. How are the two graphs in question 14 similar?

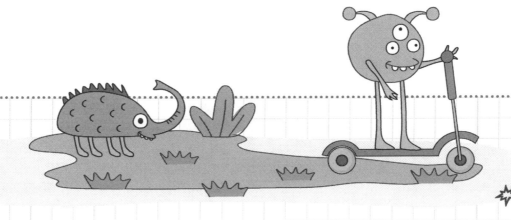

We can use what we know about displaying statistical data to summarize data sets. When we summarize data sets, we look at all of the different parts and draw conclusions about our observations.

Let's look at an example...

The line plot shows the different ages of students in summer camp. What conclusions can we draw about the summer camp based on our analysis of the data?

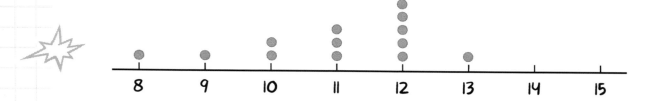

We can use what we know about shape, center, IQR, distribution and range to make observations about data.

What observations can we make?

The **shape** helps us determine that the largest age group is 12 years, but the **center** tells us that the median age is 11 years.

Practice Questions

Use the data set below to answer questions 1-6.

Class	Number of Students
Class A	25
Class B	21
Class C	23
Class D	23
Class E	8

1. What is the mean of the data set?

2. What is the median of the data set?

211

3. Which measurement is a better indicator of center for the data set?

    A. Mean   **B.** Median

4. What is the interquartile range of the data set?

5. Graph the data set using a line plot.

6. What observation can you make about the shape of the data?

Use the graph set below to answer questions 7 - 11.

82, 85, 80, 88, 95

7. What is the mean of the data set?

8. What is the median of the data set?

9. Which measurement is a better indicator of center for the data set?

    A. Mean

    B. Median

10. What is the interquartile range of the data set?

11. What observation can you make about the shape of the data?

12. Which of the following best displays the center of a data set?

A. histogram

B. box plot

5.2.B | Summarizing Data Sets

13. Which of the following best displays the number of times a value appears in a data set?

A. histogram

B. box plot

14. Which of the following best displays an outlier in a data set?

A. box plot

B. line plot

15. Which of the following best displays the median of a data set?

A. histogram

B. line plot

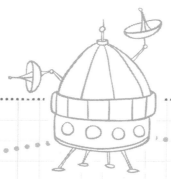

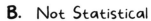

Determine whether questions 1-5 are statistical or not statistical.

1. How many phone calls did you make this week?

   A. Statistical   **B.** Not Statistical

2. How many pictures did most of the students take on the field trip?

   A. Statistical   **B.** Not Statistical

3. How many hours did you study for the test?

   A. Statistical   **B.** Not Statistical

4. How much candy did you eat last Halloween?

   A. Statistical

   B. Not Statistical

5. How much candy does a kid typically eat on Halloween?

   A. Statistical

   B. Not Statistical

The box plot below shows the number of hours the students in Mr. Najera's class studied for the math test. Use the graph to answer questions 6-9.

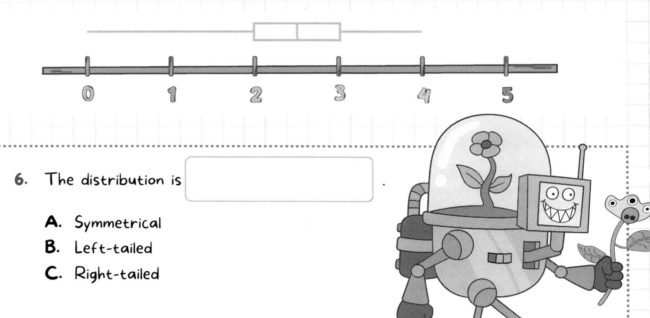

6. The distribution is [   ] .

   A. Symmetrical
   B. Left-tailed
   C. Right-tailed

7. The spread of the distribution is [   ] hours.

   A. 0 - 2
   B. 0 - 2.5
   C. 0 - 3
   D. 0 - 4

8. The center of the distribution is [   ] hours.

   A. 0 - 5
   B. 0 - 2
   C. 2 - 3
   D. 3 - 5

9. What other observations can you make by looking at the box plot?

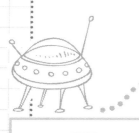

Find **6** differences and color the drawing.

The line plot below shows the age of the students in middle school. Use the graph to answer questions 10 - 15.

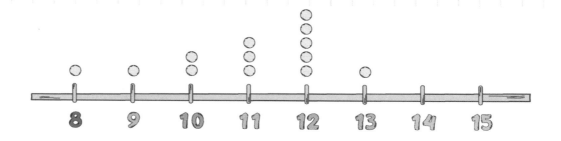

10. The distribution has [   ] .

    A. a gap

    B. an outlier

    C. none of the above

11. Describe the shape of the data.

12. What is the mean of the data? Round to the nearest whole number.

13. What is the median of the data?

14. What observations can you make about the mean and median in this data set?

15. What is the interquartile range of the data?

Use the data set below to answer questions 16 - 20

City	Inches of Snowfall
Chicago	12
New York	3
Toronto	12
Aspen	9
Buffalo	11

16. What is the mean of the data set?

17. What is the median of the data set?

5.3 | **Chapter Test**

18. Which measurement is a better indicator of center for the data set?

A. Mean

B. Median

19. What is the interquartile range of the data set?

20. What observation can you make about the shape of the data when graphed as a histogram?

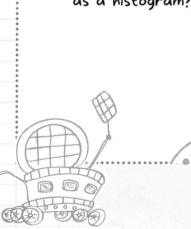

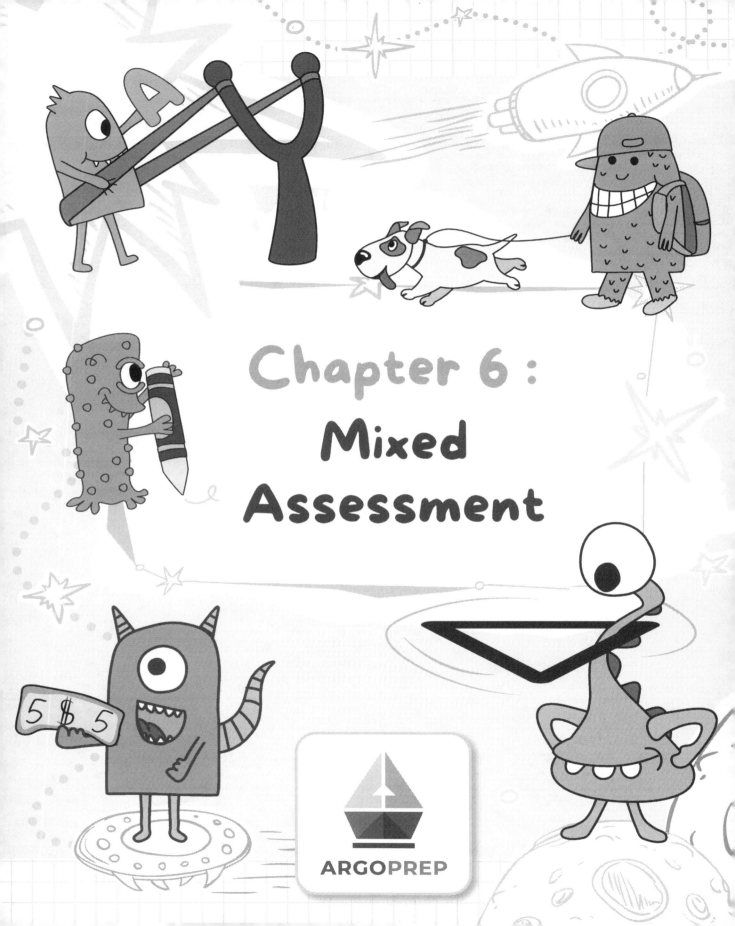

Chapter 6 :
Mixed
Assessment

ARGOPREP

1. What is the ratio of carrots to ice cream cones?

A. 4:8
B. 1:1
C. 1:8
D. 8:4

2. What is the ratio of stars to hearts?

A. 6:4
B. 2:3
C. 1:10
D. 3:2

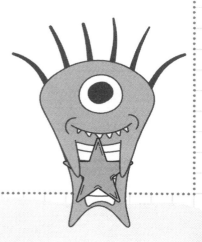

3. What is the ratio of dogs to cats?

    A. 2:6
    B. 1:3
    C. 3:1
    D. 2:8

4. What is the ratio of cats to dogs?

    A. 1:3
    B. 3:1
    C. 1:4
    D. 4:1

227

5. The ratio of teachers to students is 1:10. Explain the meaning of the ratio. How would the meaning differ if the ratio was 10:1?

6. 4 bags of popcorn cost **$8.00**. If each bag cost the same amount, how much does one bag of popcorn cost?

  A. $0.50
  B. $1.00
  C. $2.00
  D. $3.00

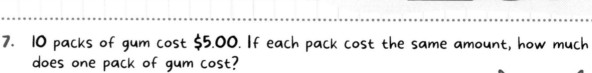

7. 10 packs of gum cost **$5.00**. If each pack cost the same amount, how much does one pack of gum cost?

  A. $0.50
  B. $0.75
  C. $1.00
  D. $2.00

8. Levi's car travels **20** miles per gallon of gas. How many miles will it travel on **20** gallons of gas?

9. At the local bakery, **30** cookies cost **$15.00**. Write a statement to describe the unit rate.

10. The recipe calls for **6** cups of sugar for every **2** cups of milk. Write a statement to describe the unit rate.

11. The rectangle below represents one whole. What percent of the rectangle is shaded?

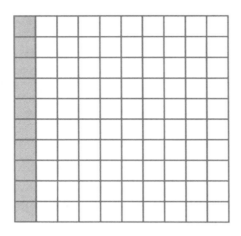

12. The rectangle below represents one whole. What percent of the rectangle is shaded?

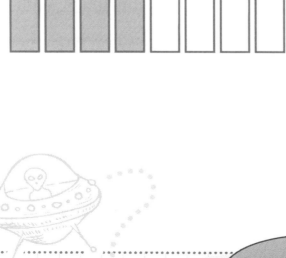

13. The school store has **60** notebooks. **5%** are composition notebooks. How many composition notebooks does the school store have?

14. The field hockey team has **20** students. **30%** of the students are sixth graders. How many sixth graders are on the team?

15. **25** out of **250** people brought dessert to the party. What percentage of people brought dessert?

16. **3** out of **60** people had ham and cheese for lunch. What percentage of people had ham and cheese for lunch?

17. $\dfrac{1}{5} \div \dfrac{3}{5} =$ ☐

18. $\dfrac{1}{8} \div \dfrac{2}{3} =$ ☐

19. How many $\dfrac{1}{8}$ cup servings are in $\dfrac{3}{4}$ of a cup?

20. How many $\dfrac{1}{4}$ miles are in $3\dfrac{1}{2}$ mile?

21. 984 ÷ 12 = [ ]

22. 475 ÷ 19 = [ ]

23. 810 ÷ 18 = [ ]

24. 360 ÷ 45 = [ ]

25. Principal Richard ordered **280** pizzas for his school. How many classes can he give **8** pizzas to?

26. 15.07 + 6.14 = [ ]

27. 5.34 + 31.2 = [ ]

28. 23.013 – 1.15 = [ ]

29. 45.23 - 2.821 = ⬚

30. 4.5 × 2.257 = ⬚

31. 26.13 × 3.4 = ⬚

32. 12.42 ÷ 1.2 = ⬚

6 | Mixed Assessment

33. 5.16 ÷ 1.2 = [   ]

34. Find the greatest common factor of 21 and 90.

35. Find the greatest common factor of 18 and 6.

36. Find the least common multiple of 16 and 12.

Use the coordinate plane below for questions 37 – 40

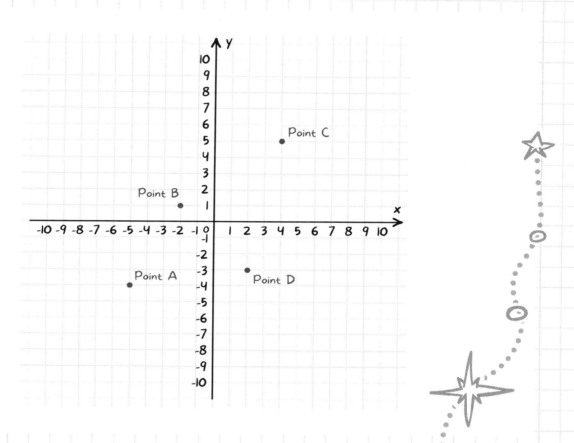

37. What are the coordinates of Point A?

38. What are the coordinates of Point B?

39. What are the coordinates of Point C?

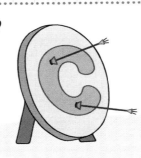

40. What are the coordinates of Point D?

41. |-9| ☐ 9

    A. >

    B. <

    C. =

42. |-6| ☐ 5

   A. >
   B. <
   C. =

43. $\frac{1}{2}$ ☐ $\frac{3}{4}$

   A. >
   B. <
   C. =

44. -5 ☐ -2

   A. >
   B. <
   C. =

45. What is the distance between (3, -1) and (3, 5)?

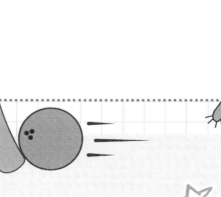

239

46. What is the distance between (2, -1) and (6, -1)?

47. $6^3 =$ [ ].

48. $2^2 =$ [ ].

49. $\left(\dfrac{1}{2}\right)^3 =$ [ ].

50. 3 x 3 x 3 x 3 x 3 . Rewrite as an exponential expression.

51. 10 x 10 x 10. Rewrite as an exponential expression.

52. Which expression has exactly 3 variables?

    A. $4x + 2y - 1$
    B. $3x$
    C. $x + 5y - c$

53. What is the coefficient in the expression $2z + \frac{1}{2}$?

    A. 2
    B. z
    C. $\frac{1}{2}$

54. How many terms are in the expression a + mn?

    A. 1

    B. 2

    C. 3

    D. 4

55. Which expression is equivalent to 1x + 2x + 3?

    A. 6x

    B. 3x + 3

    C. 6 + x2

56. Write an expression to represent x more than the product of 4 and 2.

57. Use the distributive property to write an equivalent expression for 2(d + 6y)

6 | Mixed Assessment

58. Factor $21t - 7r$ to find an equivalent expression.

59. Determine the value of x in the expression $12x = 24$.

60. In which equation does $x = 4$?

    A. $3 + x = 12$

    B. $3x = 12$

    C. $\dfrac{3}{x} = 12$

61. Jordan has d dollars. She buys 4 new shirts that each cost $14. If her total cost is all of her money, how much money did she have?

62. The number line below represents the value of x. Write an inequality for x.

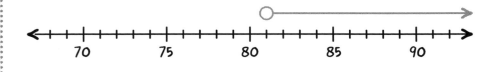

63. The number line below represents the value of x. Write an inequality for x.

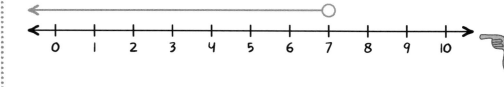

64. Kendra is making cupcakes. Write an equation for the number of chocolates she needs, c, if she has m cups of milk. She needs $\frac{1}{2}$ the amount of milk as she does chocolate.

65. Which variable is the dependent variable in the equation you created for question 64.

A. m

B. c

66. A right triangle has an area of 18 cm² and a height of 6 cm. What is the base of the triangle?

67. A rectangular prism has a base area of $\frac{2}{3}$ units² and a height of $\frac{3}{4}$ units. What is its volume?

245

Use the coordinate plane to answer questions 68 – 72

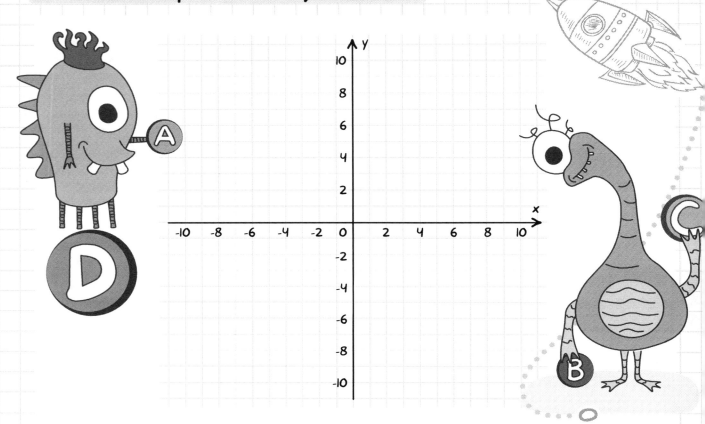

68. Draw a rectangle with vertices at A(-2, -2), B(-2, -4), C(1, -2) and D(1, -4).

69. What is the length of the rectangle?

70. What is the width of the rectangle?

71. What is the area of the rectangle?

72. What is the perimeter of the rectangle?

73. Find the area for the trapezoid below.

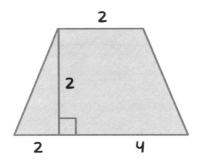

2

2

2   4

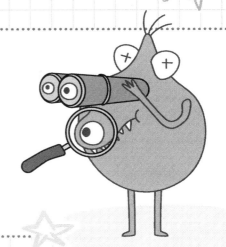

74. What is the surface area for the cube represented by the net below?

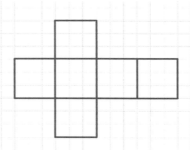

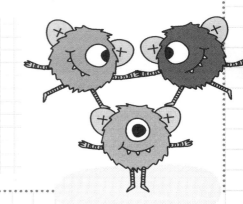

75. Sarah needs to cover a cube with foil for her science project. One edge of the cube is **2** inches. How much foil does she need to cover the cube?

76. Find the surface area of the cube below using its net.

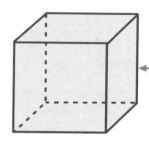

7 units

77. Find the surface area of the cube below using its net.

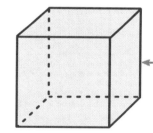

3 units

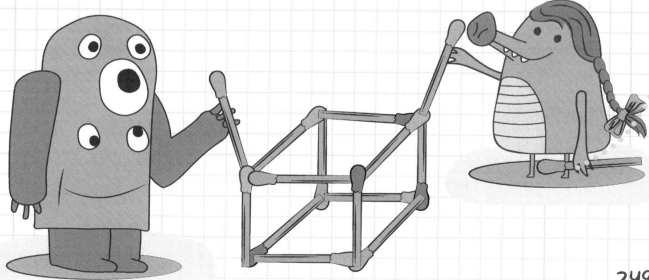

Determine whether questions 78 - 82 are statistical or not statistical.

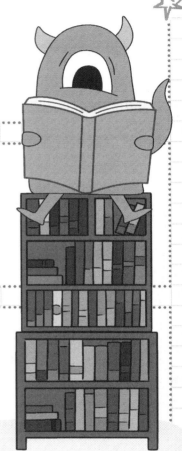

78. How old are you?

    A. Statistical

    B. Not Statistical

79. How old are the students in your class?

    A. Statistical

    B. Not Statistical

80. How many books are in a typical middle school library?

    A. Statistical

    B. Not Statistical

81. How books are in your school library?

    A. Statistical

    B. Not Statistical

82. How many teachers are in your school?

 A. Statistical
 B. Not Statistical

The box plot below shows the data collected after a race. Each value shows the number of miles the students ran. Use the box plot to answer questions 83 – 87

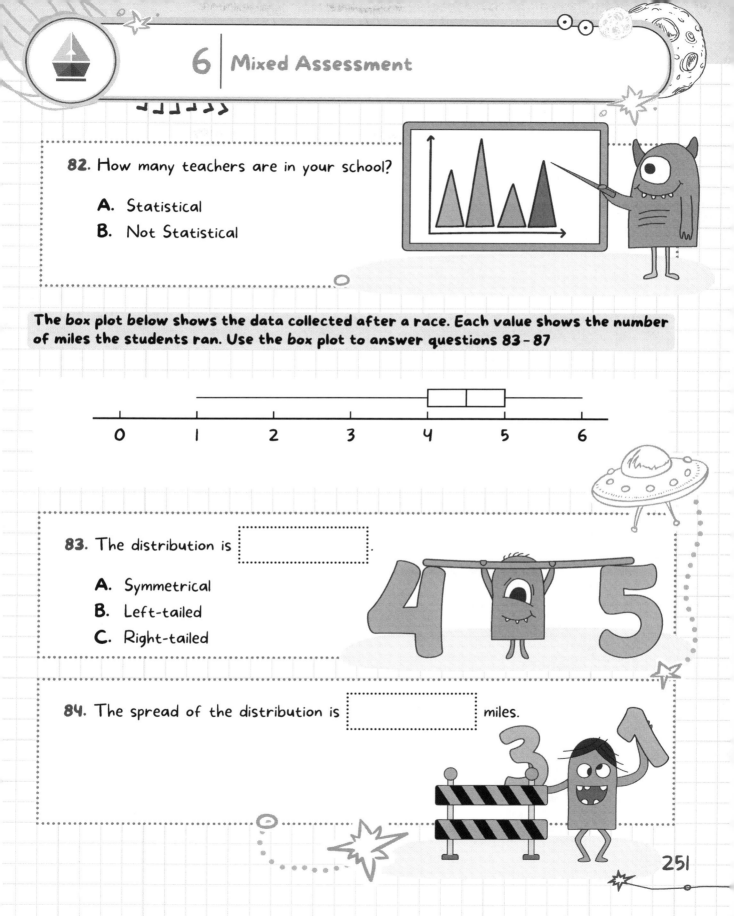

83. The distribution is [ ].

 A. Symmetrical
 B. Left-tailed
 C. Right-tailed

84. The spread of the distribution is [ ] miles.

251

85. The median of the distribution is [   ] hours.

86. What is the IQR of the data set?

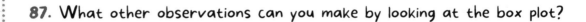

87. What other observations can you make by looking at the box plot?

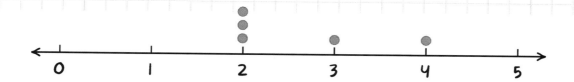

The line plot below shows the number of cookies each student ate after lunch. Use the graph to answer questions 88–93.

```
              ●
              ●
              ●       ●       ●
  ←———|———|———|———|———|———|———→
      0   1   2   3   4   5
```

88. The distribution has [   ]

   A. a gap
   B. an outlier
   C. none of the above

89. Describe the shape of the data.

90. What is the mean of the data? Round to the nearest whole number.

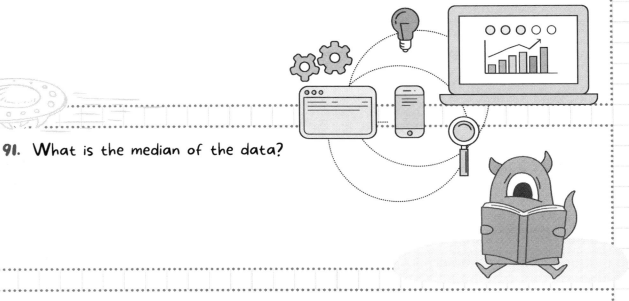

91. What is the median of the data?

92. What observations can you make about the mean and median in this data set?

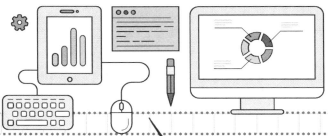

93. What is the interquartile range of the data?

Use the data set below to answer questions 94-100.

City	Inches of Rain
Chicago	2
New York	3
Toronto	3
Aspen	0
Buffalo	4

94. Draw a box plot for the data set.

95. Draw a line plot for the data set.

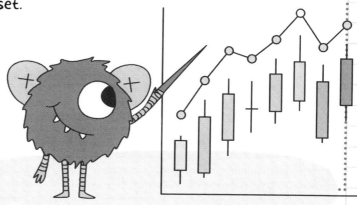

96. What is the mean of the data set?

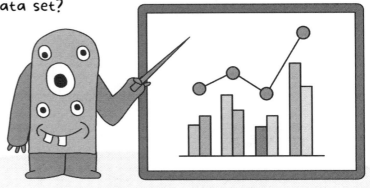

97. What is the median of the data set?

98. Which measurement is a better indicator of center for the data set?

    A. Mean
    B. Median

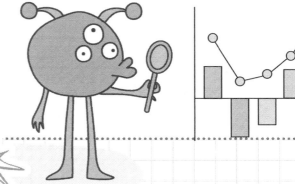

99. What is the interquartile range of the data set?

100. Which graph is a better representation of the data for someone who wants to know how much rain each city had that day? Why?

A. Line plot

B. Box plot

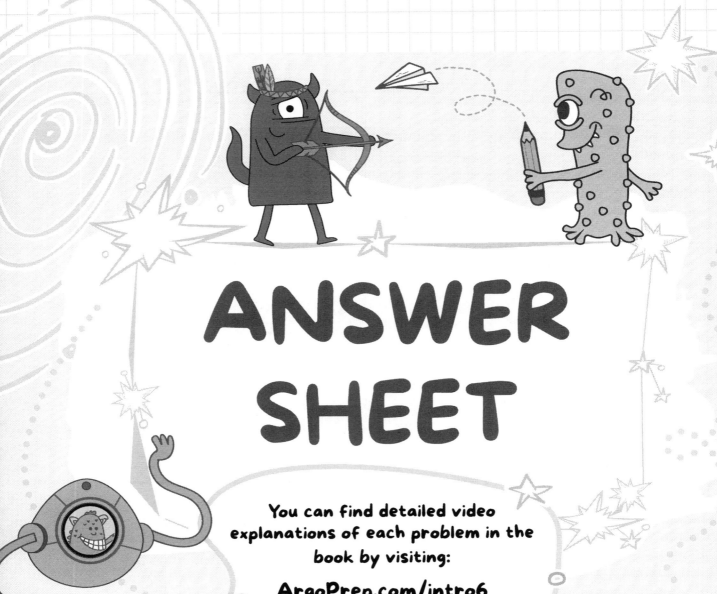

ANSWER SHEET

You can find detailed video explanations of each problem in the book by visiting:

ArgoPrep.com/intro6

ARGOPREP

To see the answer key to the entire workbook, you can easily download the answer key from our website!

*Due to the high request from parents and teachers, we have removed the answer key from the workbook so you do not need to rip out the answer key while students work on the workbook.

All you need to do is:

Step 1 - Visit our website at: www.argoprep.com/intro6

Step 2 - You will see **DOWNLOAD ANSWER SHEETS** button as well as all video explanations.

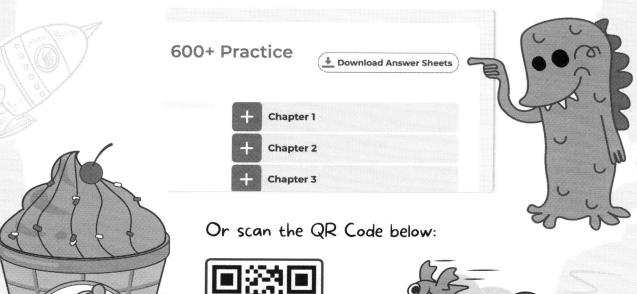

600+ Practice

⬇ Download Answer Sheets

➕ Chapter 1

➕ Chapter 2

➕ Chapter 3

Or scan the QR Code below:

KIDS SUMMER ACADEMY SERIES

ArgoPrep's Kids Summer Academy series helps prevent summer learning loss and gets students ready for their new school year by reinforcing core foundations in math, english and science. Our workbooks also introduce new concepts so students can get a head start and be on top of their game for the new school year!

SOCIAL STUDIES

Social Studies Daily Practice Workbook by ArgoPrep allows students to build foundational skills and review concepts. Our workbooks explore social studies topics in depth with ArgoPrep's 5 E's to build social studies mastery.

KIDS WINTER ACADEMY

Kids Winter Academy by ArgoPrep covers material learned in September through December so your child can reinforce the concepts they should have learned in class. We recommend using this particular series during the winter break. These workbooks include two weeks of activities for math, reading, science, and social studies.

DIPLOMA

The certificate is presented to:

_____
your name

_____
by school name

for successful completion of ArgoPrep's Introducing Math! Grade 6 workbook

Excellent work!

_____
Signature

_____
Date